IN THE WAKE OF THE "SPRAY"

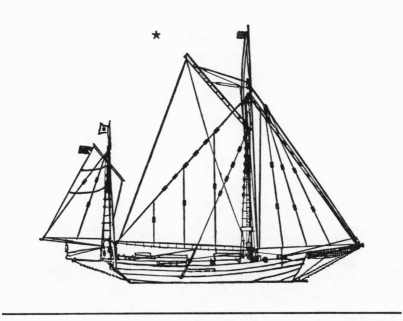

In the Wake of the SPRAY

KENNETH E. SLACK

SHERIDAN HOUSE

Published by
Sheridan House Inc.
White Plains, N.Y. 10606

Permission for the use of copyrighted material has been granted by:

Dodd, Mead & Compnay
 Inagua (The Ocean Island) by Gilbert Klingel.
Fawcett Publications, Incorporated
 Rudder Magazine
  December 1908; January, February, August 1911; December
  1927; April, May 1940; July 1950.
 Motor Boat magazine
  June 1923.
W. W. Norton & Company, Incorporated
 American Small Sailing Craft by Howard I. Chapelle.
Sheridan House Incorporated
 Capt. Joshua Slocum by Victor Slocum
 Yachting Magazine
  September 1937; June 1938; January 1951.
 Yachting Monthly, Limited
  September, October, November 1917; December 1928; April 1959.

Library of Congress
Cataloging in Publication Data

Slack, Kenneth E.
 In the wake of the Spray

Originally published: New Brunswick, N.J.: Rutgers
University Press, 1966.
Includes bibliographical references and index.
1. Spray (Sloop) I. Title.
[GV822.S62S6   1981]   623.8'22   81-9117

ISBN 0-911378-38-3   AACR2

Printed in the United States of America

To RICHARD GORDON McCLOSKEY,
who launched my search and first inspired this book

ACKNOWLEDGMENTS

My thanks are due first to those who have written on parts of the subject before me, and who have provided much of the material for this book. In particular, I am greatly indebted to the many people and institutions the world over who have helped me personally: without their assistance the data could not have been collected at all, and any value that this study may have is due largely to their contributions.

I wish especially to thank my good friend Richard Gordon McCloskey, Honorary Secretary of The Slocum Society, for his many helpful suggestions and leads for further investigations throughout the course of my search.

My thanks are also due to Harold S. Smith and Archibald B. Roosevelt for their reminiscences of sailing with Slocum on the *Spray;* and particularly to Walter Magnes Teller, who put me in touch with them and who also provided many completely new photographs of the *Spray* and copies of Slocum's letters. His valuable research on Slocum, culminating in his two recent works, *The Search for Captain Slocum* and *The Voyages of Joshua Slocum*, has brought to light much new information about the boat—an important adjunct to my own research.

I am especially grateful to the many owners of *Spray* copies who have so patiently and generously responded to my persistent requests for further information: Captain R. D. Culler of Massa-

ACKNOWLEDGMENTS

chusetts; Roger S. Strout of California; Gilbert C. Klingel of Maryland; Robert W. Carr of Vermont; Horace W. Schmahl of New York; Neal Small of New York; J. Kenneth Whitteker of New York; Captain John J. Cappelen, Jr., of Virginia; the late Captain Andrew G. Brunn of New York; Captain Eric C. Squires of New York; Charles Hinman of Gloucester, England; Henry Longmore of Nyasaland, Africa; William John Mullis of Uganda, Africa; Fritz Leisegang of Berlin, Germany; L. H. Roberts of British Columbia, Canada; and the late K. B. Johnstone of Melbourne, Australia.

In addition, I wish to thank Howard I. Chapelle, Curator of the Division of Transportation, Smithsonian Institution, The United States National Museum, for information on the origin of the *Spray*, and also for the story behind the published lines of the vessel; and Mrs. George Slocum of Detroit, for providing the rare booklet on Slocum and the *Spray* written by her husband.

I am indebted to Mrs. Catherine Woodruff of New York, niece of Victor Slocum, for information on the scale model of the *Spray* in the Peabody Museum, Salem, Massachusetts.

My thanks also to A. L. Budlong for photographs of the *Spray* at Washington, taken by his father; to Vice-Commodore Charles A. Satterthwaite of Christchurch, New Zealand, for explaining some of the more complex points of transverse stability calculations; to George M. Woodriff of Sparkman & Stephens, Inc., and Hume G. MacDougall of Cape Cod Marine Service, for helping me to trace the Oxford *Spray;* to the Librarians of the State Library in Perth and the Public Library in Sydney, Australia, and to the Secretaries of The Cruising Association and the Balboa Yacht Club, for assistance in the search; to the Editors of *Yachting Monthly, Motor Boating, The Yachting World, Le Yacht, Die Yacht, Yachting, Seacraft, The Maine Coast Fisherman, The Sydney Morning Herald*, and the Sydney *Daily News*, for publishing my letters of inquiry and for help in various ways.

KENNETH E. SLACK

Toongabbie, New South Wales
December 1965

CONTENTS

Contents

LIST OF ILLUSTRATIONS

IN THE WAKE OF THE "SPRAY"

INTRODUCTION

Some time ago I called on a friend who was finishing a boat he had built in a quiet little backwater of Sydney Harbor. She was much the same as most of the yachts in this part of the world—a good type of modern cruiser-racer—and my friend believed the design to be as good as any in the world. Although I did not fully agree with him, the delightful thing about boats is that we all have our own ideas, and are all equally right—or so it seems. The choice of a boat is like the choice of a wife—each to his own preference.

"Well," I said, "here's my idea of a boat," and I showed him a photograph of Captain Joshua Slocum's *Spray*. He studied it for a while and shook his head.

"Not for me. I can't imagine anyone wanting an old barge like that. Why, my boat here would run rings around her."

"Now, hold on," I said. "Aren't you taking a bit for granted? I admit she is hardly in the fashion these days, but if she sails as well as they say, who cares?"

"Well, I do, for one," he replied. "And, anyway, I don't

3

believe she could sail much at all; modern yachts would beat her every time." He launched into a treatise on the decided advantages of all-inboard rigs, speed to windward, and so on, but I had no time to spare and reluctantly bowed out of the discussion. I left the photograph with him and did not call again for some time. On the next visit I was surprised at the change in his attitude.

"I've been reading Slocum's *Sailing Alone Around the World* —wanted to find out a bit about the *Spray* after our talk and bought the book. I'll take back what I said—she could certainly sail, but you wouldn't have thought so from that picture. If my boat turns out as well, I'll be happy."

Since I first became interested in the *Spray* in 1951, I have been patiently collecting all the material on the boat I could find and filing it away for my own use. I never thought that anyone else would find it of much value, and still less that I could or would write a book about it. But during my research I gradually realized that other people were in fact just as interested in the *Spray* as I was, and, like me, wanted information about the vessel in addition to that in *Sailing Alone Around the World*. It was that encounter with my yachtsman friend which finally decided me to attempt this book, not only to provide information about the *Spray*, but also to help correct some of the popular misconceptions about her.

Slocum wrote more for the general reader than for the sailing man. Although a lot can be gleaned from his references here and there to the *Spray*'s performance, the technical side of his voyage was played down. Having been a professional sailor himself, perhaps he did not realize the interest of amateurs, past and present, in the working of his little vessel. In one bad gale, he scudded under forestaysail only, sheeted flat amidships, and towed a hawser over each quarter to break the great Pacific combers. This practice has since been used by yachts with great success, yet Slocum puts forward no hard-and-fast theories—as, for example, those of Captain Voss with his sea anchor. Slocum mentions only incidentally his use of a sea anchor in the last and worst of the many great storms he passed through, yet his son tells us he always kept it ready

4

and often used it. He has scarcely even a remark to offer on the relative merits of sloop and yawl rigs, though he takes considerable trouble, less than halfway through his voyage, to change to the latter in preparation for the stormy regions of Cape Horn. The only dogma of which he delivers himself is the danger of overhangs for offshore craft:

Our young yachtsmen, pleasuring in the "lilies of the sea," very naturally will not think favorably of my craft. They have a right to their opinion, while I stick to mine. They will take exception to her short ends, the advantage of these being most apparent in a heavy sea. . . . Some even say that I might have improved the shape of her stern. I do not know about that. The water leaves her run sharp after bearing her to the last inch, and no suction is formed by undue cutaway.

Smooth-water sailors say, "Where is her overhang?" They never crossed the Gulf Stream in a nor'easter and they do not know what is best in all weathers. For your life, build no fantail overhang on a craft going offshore.[1]

This was included in the Appendix, the only juicy tidbit of technical information in the whole book. Such brevity on matters concerning the *Spray* only whets one's appetite for more, and many people, impressed with Slocum's few statements about her performance, have no doubt wished for some detailed information.

Victor Slocum's biography of his father, *The Life and Voyages of Captain Joshua Slocum*, contains some new *Spray* material, and the more recent works by Walter Magnes Teller, *The Search for Captain Slocum* and *The Voyages of Joshua Slocum*, although dealing principally with the man himself, also have additional data on the boat. There are many previously unpublished photographs of the *Spray* in these books, but little information to satisfy those wanting to know more about her behavior.

In the course of my research on the *Spray*, I have received a great many letters from people also interested in the boat itself, some merely wishing to supplement the notes in the captain's book, others wanting plans and specifications sufficient to build copies of the *Spray*.

5

Inquiries from people wanting to build have come from America, England, France, Portugal, Poland, South Africa, Peru, and Australia. In these days of increasing national tensions, such world-wide interest is especially heartening.

A New York man wrote:

I have just completed reading Captain Slocum's report of his voyage around the world alone. It was a very interesting book and Captain Slocum certainly was an admirable man. My wife and I are very much interested in boats and boating and although we've never done much sailing it is our dream to someday have a boat of our own with which we might do some extensive world traveling. We are going to explore every possible way of getting our own boat even to building it ourselves. The *Spray* seems to be ideal for our use. Is it possible to obtain the construction plans and, if so, how, where, and the approximate cost?

So, despite all the years since Captain Slocum made his renowned world voyage, there is still much interest in the little vessel that bore him so bravely. The main purpose of this book is to present all the available information on the *Spray* and her copies. It is essentially a personal story, this story of the *Spray* —of technical findings interspersed with opinions. The subjective approach may not appeal to those interested only in facts and figures; this is not, nor was it intended to be, a scientific treatise—but rather the account of a labor of love through which the dream of one *Spray* enthusiast has, on paper at least, been partially realized.

Though much can be—and has been—said for and against the *Spray*, nothing can detract from her achievement. The pity is that this is not more widely appreciated. If my small effort in any way helps to further stimulate interest in the old vessel for her own sake, I shall feel amply rewarded.

1

IN THE BEGINNING

As the tram rattled along, I sat back and looked through the small, grimy window into the growing darkness outside. It was overcast and raining heavily, and the bright headlights of passing cars picked out long fingers of cold white amid myriad sparkling drops slanting to the ground. The shop signs reflected red and green in the wet, black mirror of bitumen, and through the closed canvas doors on the weather side came the familiar sounds of peak-hour traffic on this cheerless mid-winter evening. As usual at this time, the tram was crowded with students homeward bound from that stately mass of great, gray stone atop a hill just outside the city of Sydney. It had been a tiring day at the university, full of lectures which, for the most part, I found extremely boring. Somehow, sometime, I might make that degree yet, though it seemed a long way off. Then I could shut my textbooks for good, and settle down to a professional career. But was this, after all, what I really wanted? Was my ambition a steady nine-to-five job, offering security and advancement—or was there something else? I closed my eyes and let my mind drift away from the chatter in the tram, the noises of the traffic, and all the cacophony of the city—let it drift far away into another world, the vastness of the South Pacific.

. . . My inner ear caught a fresh, new sound, and to my mind's eye there came the vision of my secret dream. With a hiss and swirl of white foam at her bow, a small yacht was forging her way across the ocean, sails bellying to the warm trade winds. One man sat naked at the helm, his skin nut-brown in the tropical sun, and beneath a shock of flaxen hair, his features showed strong and determined. A true individualist this—a singlehanded sailor. Raising his face to the sky, he laughed aloud to the sun and the sea, for was it not good to be alive? Here, remote from the cares of civilization, this man rejoiced in the breath of the warm wind, the sway of the ship moving with the sea, the slow dignity of sunrise and sunset. Alone in this virgin world he felt at peace. Time stood still. This was a voyage of the spirit. . . .

The tram jolted to a stop, and I waited for the compartment to empty before stepping out, with briefcase and umbrella, into the night. Heavy traffic streamed past in the rain and the busy world of the city enveloped me again.

I had some time to spare before the train was due, and went into a bookshop near by. I wandered around looking for something of interest and came on a little paperbacked volume sitting out on its own in front of a pile of others. The colored cover caught my eye. At the wheel of a sailing yacht stood an elderly man, knee-deep in the water pouring over the decks. All around were foam-flecked seas, and astern a mountainous coast showed dark against an ominous sky. *Sailing Alone Around the World* by Joshua Slocum was the title, and I picked it up to have a quick look through.

Twenty minutes later I suddenly realized I had missed my train, and the shop was getting ready to close. I had been so enthralled glancing through the little book that everything else had been forgotten. But I could not have cared less; I had just fallen in love—with a boat. I remembered my secret dream as I paid two-and-six for the book that was to influence the course of my life.

8

2

THE STORY OF THE "SPRAY"

Joshua Slocum was one of the great American sailing-ship captains. He had command of some of the finest ships of his day, but it is in connection with a far smaller and more modest vessel that he is best remembered. It was in 1895 that Slocum, at the age of fifty-one—when most men have long since given up adventuring—set out from Boston, Massachusetts, in a 37-foot sloop, the *Spray*. Three years later, the captain moored his little ship in his home port of Fairhaven. For the first time, a man had sailed alone around the world.

In 1909, Slocum set out once more in the *Spray*, this time on a voyage to South America. He and his ship were never seen again, and no clue to his fate was ever found.

Sailing Alone Around the World is Captain Joshua Slocum's imperishable memorial. In the introduction to the Pan Books edition of the work, the well-known author and yachtsman Arthur Ransome wrote:

Sailing Alone Around the World is one of the immortal books. Joshua Slocum was the first man to sail round the world in a small boat with none but himself as captain, mate and crew. Other men may repeat the feat. No other man can be the first. Captain Slocum's place in history is as secure as Adam's. So long as men sail the seas they will be interested in that first single-handed circumnavigation and will wish to read the book in which the story of that voyage is told. It has inspired and will inspire many other voyages. It has illumined and will illumine the dreams of many boat owners who can never hope to make a longer voyage than they can cram into a fortnight's holiday. It has been and will be a delight to many who can voyage only in their own armchairs.[1]

This is not the place to say very much about Slocum or his book, both of which have been admirably covered by Walter Magnes Teller in *The Search for Captain Slocum*. The story is not only the record of the best-known small-boat voyage ever undertaken, it is also a classic of literature. Slocum displays not only his great capacity as a writer, but a little of himself as well. Here is the simple and sincere story of a nature lover and philosopher. Take this passage, for instance:

The wind freshened, and the *Spray* rounded Deer Island light at the rate of seven knots. Passing it, she squared away direct for Gloucester where she was to procure some fishermen's stores. Waves dancing joyously across Massachusetts Bay met the sloop coming out to dash themselves instantly into myriads of sparkling gems that hung about her breast at every surge. The day was perfect, the sunlight clear and strong. Every particle of water thrown into the air became a gem, and the *Spray*, making good her name as she dashed ahead, snatched necklace after necklace from the sea, and as often threw them away. We have all seen miniature rainbows about a ship's prow, but the *Spray* flung out a bow of her own that day, such as I had never seen before. Her good angel had embarked on the voyage; I so read it in the sea.[2]

In a review of the first English edition of the book in 1900, Sir Edwin Arnold wrote: "The tale is true from first to last, written in a style plain as a marlin-spike, and yet full of touches which show what hidden poetry and passionate love of Nature were in the soul of this 'blue-nose' skipper. . . ." [3]

There is something entrancing in this story of a man and the boat he built with his own hands to sail around the world, with Nature alone as companion. Who has not dreamed of doing this very thing? To exchange the deadening humdrum of petty convention and collective scramble for the wild freedom of the open sea, to taste for a time the spice of adventure in the call of the ocean wind, is to find both stimulation and consolation. The sophistication and superficiality of our complex existence imprisons our being. Alone, in the solitude of nature, in the vast blue infinity of sea and sky that is the matrix of creation, man's primordial being awakes as body and mind are cleansed by water, wind, and sun. In this return to the primitive, man draws closer to the real essence of life, finding peace, strength of spirit, and— himself. No escape *from* reality this, but rather *to* it. The wide loneliness of the great ocean breeds a humility that is good for the soul.

The finest tribute to Slocum I have ever read was written by Thomas Fleming Day, former editor of *Rudder*. It is in the nature of an epitaph and deserves to be quoted here:

Slocum's story is a remarkable one; I do not mean as the story of a voyage but as a piece of writing. It is written in a pure narrative style, absolutely devoid of any disfigurements betraying effort, and flows from page to page like a wind-favored tide. It is worthy to be placed beside any narrative writing in any language. . . . your great-grandchildren will be advised to read Slocum's voyage, as a specimen of clean, pure narrative, just as today they read Robinson Crusoe or The Voyage of the Beagle. Peace to Captain Slocum wherever he may sleep, for he deserves at least one whispered tribute of prayer from every sailorman for what he did to rob the sea of its bad name; and for such a man, who loved every cranny of her dear old blue heart, who for years made her wind-swept stretches his home and highway, what is more fitting than an ocean burial?

Not in old bannered abbeys are her children laid to rest,
 With the trophies of the chisel and the bronzes of the wall;
She takes them from their cradles to lie within her breast,
 To rest unchanged forever in that vast and lightless hall.

The loftiest of temples, the stateliest of domes,
 Where the master-minds of nations are laid with pomp and pride,

11

Are but low and spaceless fabrics beside the Fane of Foams,
  Whose nave no man has put to rule, whose floors are ocean wide.

It mocks in its magnificence the sepulchre of kings;
  The glory of the purple and the splendor of the bier,
And all the brass and marble are but mean and gaudy things
  Beside the splendid trappings that the dead inherit here.[4]

3

ALONE AROUND THE WORLD

Slocum and the *Spray* came together quite by chance. Thrown on hard times by the lack of square-riggers—"on the beach," as the old sailors used to say—he was on the point of going to work at a Boston shipyard when he met an old friend. Eben Pierce was a retired whaling captain, and he said to Slocum: "Come to Fairhaven and I'll give you a ship. But . . . she wants some repairs." [1] The next day, Slocum found that his friend "had something of a joke" on him. The "ship" proved to be a very ancient sloop called the *Spray*, which was lying in a field, some distance from the water. She was in a bad way through long neglect, but there was something about her that immediately impressed Slocum, and he decided there and then to rebuild her.

Slocum deals only briefly with the actual building, but his son Victor goes into more detail in his biography. The old *Spray* was a centerboarder, but knowing that this arrangement would be a weakness at sea, Slocum fitted a solid keel in its place. Near by was a stand of pasture white oak, a particularly tough

13

variety of oak once common to the shores of New England. The captain felled the trees himself and shaped the backbone of the new *Spray*. During the whole procedure, the form of the old vessel was carefully preserved. The floor timbers were sawn across without disturbing the garboards and the old keel removed in sections, leaving the original stem and sternpost intact. After a new keel had been fitted, a whole new set of floor timbers was installed and the old garboards fastened to them temporarily. The frame timbers were steamed, pre-bent, and fastened temporarily against the old planking for about a third of the vessel's length. The new stem piece, stem knee, and apron were then set up and fastened to the keel.

It was a great day in the *Spray* "shipyard" when the new stem was installed. It marked the end of the first stage of construction. Whaling captains from nearby New Bedford took much interest in the *Spray*, and often dropped by for a "gam." In their opinion, the new stem was "fit to smash ice." A new sternpost, deadwood, and transom were then set up, and the rest of the frame timbers installed. The planks were of Georgia pine— now generally called pitch pine—an inch and a half thick. Those at the turn of the bilge were three inches thick and took the place of the usual inside stringers. The planking was copper riveted to the frames, while the butts were through-bolted. Slocum records that about a thousand bolts were used in the construction, all being set up with nuts and washers.

The bulwarks were built up of white oak stanchions, 14 inches high, and covered with ⅞-white pine. The stanchions were mortised through a 2-inch covering board and caulked with thin cedar wedges. The deck was 1½-by-3-inch white pine spiked to 6-by-6-inch beams of Georgia pine placed 3 feet apart.

There were two cabin trunks, one about 6 feet square, serving as a galley, and one further aft, about 10 feet by 12, for a cabin. Both of these rose about 3 feet above the deck to give full headroom. In the space along the starboard side of the cabin under the deck, a bunk was fitted, and shelves were built for the storage of small gear. A stanchion in the middle of the cabin provided against the top being smashed down by heavy seas. Around its base a circular table was built, within easy reach

14

of the bunk. Between cabin and galley was the midship hold, about 5 feet fore and aft by the entire width of the vessel under decks. Here was ample storage for food and water. Forward of the galley and under the foredeck were two bunks with room for the stowage of spare sails, anchor chain, spare anchor, and other gear.

After he completed the hull, Slocum set about caulking ship. Cotton was used, with a thread of oakum driven on top of it. The seams were then payed with a filling cement, the bottom given two coats of copper paint, and the topsides and bulwarks two coats of white lead. The rudder was shipped and painted, and the next day the *Spray* was launched. It was a great moment for the old captain, who wrote: "As she rode at her ancient, rust-eaten anchor, she sat on the water like a swan." [2] When finished, her dimensions were 36 feet 9 inches OA, 14 feet 2 inches in the beam, 4 feet 2 inches deep in the hold, her tonnage being 9 tons net and 12 and $7\frac{1}{100}$ ton gross.

Under the sheers farther down the harbor the mast, a smart stick of New Hampshire spruce, was stepped and stayed. Sails were bent and, with Captain Slocum and Captain Pierce on board, the *Spray* flew off across Buzzards Bay on a trial trip. Everything proved satisfactory and she was made ready for sea. The great adventure was just beginning.

Slocum left Boston on 24th April 1895. "A thrilling pulse beat high in me. My step was light on deck in the crisp air." So he wrote in his book.[3] The first stage of the trip was a shakedown cruise to Yarmouth, Nova Scotia. Here he took on plenty of supplies and checked over the rigging for the long trans-Atlantic haul ahead. He sailed with a fair wind and the *Spray* reeled off 1,200 miles in the first eight days from Nova Scotia.

Slocum found he could adjust the sails so that the *Spray* steered herself, running for days, sometimes weeks on end, with the wheel lashed. That was a tremendous boon to the single-hander, and solved the problem of rest and sleep.

Eighteen days after passing the tip of Nova Scotia, the *Spray* put in at Fayal, in the Azores. Here the captain took aboard fresh food. Not long after putting to sea again, he dined too copiously on fresh plums and a white cheese which he had been given on the island of Pico, and he soon was taken with cramps. With difficulty he managed to double-reef the mainsail, and then threw himself on the cabin floor in great pain. He became delirious.

When I came to, as I thought, from my swoon, I realized that the sloop was plunging into a heavy sea, and looking out of the companionway, to my amazement I saw a tall man at the helm. His rigid hand, grasping the spokes of the wheel, held them as in a vise. One may imagine my astonishment. His rig was that of a foreign sailor, and the large red cap he wore was cockbilled over his left ear, and all was set off with shaggy black whiskers. He would have been taken for a pirate in any part of the world. . . . "Señor," said he, doffing his cap, 'I have come to do you no harm. . . . I am one of Columbus's crew. . . . I am the pilot of the *Pinta* come to aid you. Lie quiet, señor captain," he added, "and I will guide your ship to-night." [4]

Throughout the gale, the ghost pilot guided the *Spray*, and when the captain recovered, nothing was amiss; the *Spray* was still on her course. Later, Slocum threw overboard all the plums in the vessel, "by inspiration."

At Gibraltar, the *Spray* fell among friends. For the duration of her three weeks' stay, she was the guest of the British Navy, and Slocum was treated like a hero. "That one should like Gibraltar would go without saying. How could one help loving so hospitable a place? Vegetables twice a week and milk every morning came from the palatial grounds of the admiralty." [5]

Slocum had originally planned to sail through the Mediterranean and into the Red Sea via the Suez Canal, thence east-about around the world. At Gibraltar the British authorities warned him of the danger of pirates along this route, particularly for a lone hand. He accordingly decided to go west-about. Leaving Gibraltar, he headed southwestward down the African coast; but he was not to avoid pirates so easily. Off the coast of Morocco, a felucca gave chase, and a grim race ensued with Slocum's life as the stake. The wind was blowing a gale, but he drove the *Spray* on under full sail, with the felucca steadily gaining. The *Spray* was carrying too much sail for safety, and it was a choice of reef or be dismasted. Slocum decided to reef, and as the felucca bore down on him, it suddenly broached on the crest of a great wave and was dismasted. The same wave snapped the *Spray*'s boom, but the pirates were too busy saving their own craft to pursue her again. After emergency repairs, Slocum continued on.

Just north of the equator, the *Spray* entered the gloomy region of the doldrums, and for ten days battled calms, light variable winds, squalls, and thunderstorms. Once out of these, however, the southeast trade wind filled her sails and sent her over the sea toward the coast of Brazil.

Forty days after Gibraltar, the *Spray* reached Pernambuco and then sailed on down the South American coast, stopping off for a time in Rio de Janeiro and putting in at Montevideo for Christmas. He sailed up the River Plate to Buenos Aires, where he spent New Year's Day of 1896 with old friends from his trading days. While continuing down the coast of Patagonia toward the Strait of Magellan, the *Spray* encountered a great tidal wave which roared down upon her in a storm. Slocum had just time to drop sails and spring into the rigging before an avalanche of green water submerged the entire vessel. For a moment, nothing was visible except the mast and rigging to which he clung; then the *Spray* shook herself free and bobbed to the surface. Rounding Cape Virgins, at the eastern entrance to the Strait, the *Spray* was struck by a southwest gale. For thirty hours it blew hard, but the little vessel held on stoutly and was not blown out to sea. She managed to beat through to the Chilean coaling station of Punta Arenas. Here the captain was warned of the danger of savage Indians farther west and was advised to ship some extra hands to fight them. No one seemed willing to join him, however, so he loaded his guns and acquired a bag of carpet tacks, "worth more than all the fighting men and dogs of Tierra del Fuego." [6]

The passage through the Strait was not easy. Here Slocum had his first experience with the terrible squalls called williwaws. "They were compressed gales of wind that Boreas handed down over the hills in chunks. A full-blown williwaw will throw a ship, even without sail on, over on her beam ends. . . ." [7]

17

There were also several encounters with Indians, and Slocum kept his gun always close at hand.

On emerging into the Pacific, the *Spray* met one of Cape Horn's equinoctial gales, which blew with terrific force from the northwest. Stripped of her sails, she ran off before the wind under bare poles through the raging seas. The only safe course lay in keeping her before the wind, and as she drove southeast, Slocum thought he might have to sail round the Horn and return to the Atlantic. But at last the storm abated before he had back-tracked completely, and he found a passage into the Strait. In his second trip through the Strait of Magellan, the captain had a sharp brush with savage Indians. At night he sprinkled the deck with carpet tacks, seeing to it that not a few of them stood "business end" up! Of the results he wrote: "A pretty good Christian will whistle when he steps on the 'commercial end' of a carpet-tack; a savage will howl and claw the air, and that was just what happened that night about twelve o'clock, while I was asleep in the cabin. . . . I had no need of a dog, they howled like a pack of hounds. I had hardly use for a gun. They jumped pell-mell, some into their canoes and some into the sea, to cool off, I suppose. . . ." [8]

The *Spray* finally cleared Cape Pillar for the second time, and sailed out into the Pacific. The hardest part of his world voyage now lay behind Slocum. Although many singlehanded circumnavigations have been made since, Slocum's feat of sailing alone through the worst part of Tierra del Fuego has never been repeated. It is not likely that it will be.

Once again Slocum had the vast ocean all around him. Gone were the rocks and the cold winds, and he set a course for Juan Fernandez—Robinson Crusoe's famous island off the coast of Chile. Summer lay ahead for the *Spray*. "The wind . . . had moderated, and roaring seas had turned to gossiping waves that rippled and pattered against her sides as she rolled among them, delighted with their story." [9] At remote Juan Fernandez Slocum spent many happy days but nothing pleased him more than a visit to the home and very cave where Robinson Crusoe's prototype, Alexander Selkirk, had lived in complete solitude for over four years.

Leaving Juan Fernandez, Slocum set sail for Samoa. The southeast trades blew hard and the *Spray* sped along with a bone in her mouth. For a whole month she held her course, and Slocum was able once more to sit and read, mend his clothes, cook his meals, and eat them in peace. "I made companionship with what there was around me, sometimes with the universe and sometimes with my own insignificant self; but my books were always my friends, let fail all else. Nothing could be easier or more restful than my voyage in the trade-winds." [10] The lone navigator sighted the Marquesas Islands forty-three days out and confirmed his longitude, then pressed on for Samoa where he dropped anchor after another twenty-nine days. He had been seventy-two days alone at sea with making port.

The captain enjoyed himself greatly in Samoa. He remarked that the farther he got from civilization, the less people cared about money. The islanders only had to put out their hand and take what Nature provided for them. A native chief expressed the simple philosophy of his people and, to Slocum, his words rang true: "Dollar, dollar, . . . white man know only dollar. . . . On the tree there is fruit. Let the day go by; why should we mourn over that? There are millions of days coming. The breadfruit is yellow in the sun, and from the cloth-tree is Taloa's gown. Our house, which is good, cost but the labour of building it, and there is no lock on the door." [11]

The captain paid a visit to Mrs. Robert Louis Stevenson at Vailima and saw the old desk where the great writer used to work.

At the end of six weeks, Slocum was again ready for deep water. He set sail for Australia, passing north of Fiji, and arrived at Newcastle in the teeth of a gale. Sailing south to Sydney, he found the harbor "blooming" with yachts. The summer season was approaching and it seemed to Slocum that everybody owned a boat. After several months, Slocum continued around the Australian coast to Melbourne, with a pleasant but nonpaying stop-off ashore for a bit of gold prospecting on the way.

Slocum's plan had been to sail westward around Cape Leeuwin direct for Mauritius on his way home. However, adverse winds and ice drifting up from the Antarctic foretold a rough and uncomfortable passage, and he decided instead to take advantage of favorable winds and go northward through Torres Strait. The season was not yet right for this course and the captain sailed over to have a look at Tasmania. Leaving the *Spray* berthed on the beach at a small jetty in Launceston, he took the opportunity to rusticate amid the forests and streams.

At Devonport the *Spray* was hauled out and a fresh coat of copper paint applied to her bottom. Meanwhile, the friendly people gave him wine, jams, jellies, and cheese. Well provisioned, he sailed north along the Great Barrier Reef that fringes Australia's eastern coast to Thursday Island in the Torres Strait. Here he attended a grand aboriginal corroboree which was part of the festivities marking the Queen's jubilee. As he sailed through the tropic waters of the Arafura Sea, he idled on deck until late at night, watching the phosphorescence. "The sea, where the sloop disturbed it, seemed all ablaze, so that by its light I could see the smallest articles on deck, and her wake was a path of fire." [12]

Slocum sailed on across the Indian Ocean, the *Spray* steering herself as usual in the trade winds, and dropped anchor in a lagoon of the Cocos Islands. Hundreds of children of all ages and sizes mustered at the jetty to welcome Slocum ashore, and he was much impressed by the overall friendliness of this island community. Continuing on to Rodriguez Island, Slocum again took in fresh provisions, including beef, sweet potatoes, and pomegranates. His course then took him to Mauritius and on to South Africa. Gales sweeping round the Cape of Good Hope gave the *Spray* a rough time, and Christmas Day was spent in heavy seas off the pitch of the Cape.

Reaching Cape Town, Slocum left the *Spray* in charge of the port authorities, and spent three months seeing the country with the aid of a free railroad pass given him by the government. He even had an interview with President Kruger, the great Boer leader, who thought the world was flat. Kruger would not believe that the captain was sailing around the world. " 'You don't mean *round* the world,' said the president; 'it is impossible. You mean *in* the world. . . .' " [13]

Leaving Cape Town, Slocum set sail on the final leg of his

voyage to America. He put in at St. Helena, Napoleon's famous island of exile, and on departure, was given a goat. As soon as the animal got his sea legs, Slocum had no peace. He was the worst pirate encountered on the whole voyage, and among other things chewed into ropes, ate the captain's chart of the West Indies, and topped it off by eating his best straw hat. To save the *Spray* and himself from further depredation, Slocum marooned his unwelcome passenger at the next port of call, Ascension Island.

A fortnight after leaving Ascension, the *Spray* crossed her own outward-bound track. She had now encircled the globe. The Captain steered for the West Indies, but had to rely on memory when nearing land. The chart eaten by the St. Helena goat was a big loss, and Slocum had some anxious moments. Clearing from St. John, Antigua, the *Spray* was bound for the United States. For eight days she lay becalmed in the horse latitudes. There was no wind at all and the sea was quite smooth. "Evening after evening during this time I read by the light of a candle on deck." [14] Off Fire Island the *Spray* was struck by a tornado, which had swept New York City only an hour before. It was the climax storm of the voyage, but the *Spray* rode it out under bare poles, lying to a sea anchor.

On June 27, 1898, Slocum cast anchor in Newport Harbor, to end a voyage of more than 46,000 miles around the world. He had been away three years and two months.

4

THE DREAM AND I

Sailing Alone Around the World was not the first sea book I had read, and there had been other dream ships too before the *Spray* won my heart. The first book I can remember that shaped the misty ideals of my own boat into a more concrete form was that grand tale by Rudyard Kipling, *Captains Courageous*. Thereafter, my vessel-to-be became a schooner, possibly 60 or 70 feet long, modeled on the *We're Here* of the story. To me, there is still something very attractive about the schooner rig; it brings visions of romance and adventure—fishing fleets plying the fog-shrouded shallows of the Grand Banks; blackbirder traders among the sun-drenched South Sea islands.

Later, a friend at high school lent me his copy of *The Fight of the "Firecrest"* by Alain Gerbault—the record of a lone Atlantic crossing in a 39-foot cutter. My dream ship then shrank to a more manageable size, about 35 to 40 feet, and changed her rig from schooner to cutter. Not that I meant to copy the *Firecrest*, which was built as a racing boat, but a vessel of her general size seemed big enough for a floating home, yet not too large for

22

one man to handle. Anyway, it was a start and, on paper, my dream ship began to take shape. Then came the sloop *Spray*, and here, at last, was a boat that fitted in with everything I wanted.

The story of the *Spray* is a fascinating one; it has probably fired the imaginations of thousands of people. As has been true with many others, I fell under the spell of the old captain's sincere, simplehearted account of a lone voyage around the world at the first reading. Well can I remember poring over the little Appendix, "Lines and Sail-Plan of the *Spray*." Days and nights were spent reading and rereading the words of a man who had spent a lifetime upon the sea. One particular sentence remains in my mind: "I have given in the plans of the *Spray* the dimensions of such a ship as I should call seaworthy in all conditions of weather and on all seas." [1] That rings as true to me today as it did that first time I picked up the book, many years ago.

So it was that as a direct outcome of reading old Slocum's narrative, there came the burning desire to build my own *Spray* and sail in her to far-off lands. How many such dreams have been inspired by the same story of the first and greatest single-handed circumnavigation?

Unlike those many others who have found the boat of their choice in some streamlined modern hull, my dream ship became the *Spray*, the beamiest and shallowest of them all—an old tub whose design was the result of chance, whose very origin was shrouded in mystery. Tradition had it she was an oysterman a century before Slocum found her. This would date her at about 1800 or earlier. To choose such a craft in preference to one of modern design would surely be, at most, the height of foolishness and, at least, sheer retrocession, for who would dare consider the development in yacht design over the last century as being anything but true progress? Who, indeed? In view of the fact that many copies of the *Spray* have been built and many still are being planned, there must be a few people prepared to forego the fruits of architectural achievement.

I plead guilty to being one of those odd individuals, and it might clarify the position somewhat if I venture to express some

23

personal opinions on the worth of the *Spray* design, modern progress and all notwithstanding. The experts who know, or think they do, may credit my dogmatic beliefs to lay ignorance, if they like.

At the outset, I am going to say that overall seaworthiness—the form of boats to harmoniously "fit" both wind and sea—has been improved not one jot by all the ingenious paper mathematics of the last half century. It has always seemed rather remarkable to me that improvement in only one aspect of boat performance has been taken as indicative of improvement in performance as a whole. One might say, with some justification, that the entire aspect of theoretical design since its earliest beginnings has been concentrated on windward behavior. In view of modern man's seemingly insatiable desire for speed and "efficiency" in all phases of his civilization, it is not surprising that this feature of boat design should now be so emphasized to the virtual exclusion of most others. However, mere speed and efficiency of technological development are not always infallible criteria of improvement in human society; neither is the improvement in windward performance (which is the main difference between craft of today and those of yesterday) necessarily an indication of overall improvement. The production of a racing machine better able to thrash to windward, everything tense and strained, occupants included, typifies the spirit of our age—a spirit in discord with natural motion. . . .

In developing craft with unparalleled ability on the wind, the time-tested qualities of the old vessels for off the wind sailing and general seaworthiness have not been bettered in the least, but rather worsened. The older craft were not designed as we know the word; they were modeled by eye, almost by an instinct, one might say, bred out of the experience of generations of seafaring, and culminated in a form best suited to its intended purpose. The centuries of intuitive knowledge embodied in such vessels may not lightly be disregarded in favor of the comparatively short term, rapidly changing paper theories which imbue everyone with superficial ideas of progress. Of course, a boat cannot be perfect both on and off the wind; the qualities required by each case are as different as chalk and cheese. It

24

is a question of the best compromise, and this will ever be a point of controversy.

It is well to bear in mind that the major part of sea exploration took place long before so-called scientific design was ever thought of and in vessels rated hopeless by present-day standards. This would surely show, if any proof were needed, that most ocean work must be off the wind; it is dictated by practical necessity, convenience, and plain human survival. If this were not so, the performance of sailing boats on the wind would have been improved long since. Where, then, the justification, either in theory or in practice, for this emphasis on work *against* the elements rather than *with* them, or the all too prevalent assumption that the type of design to which this gives rise necessarily is an improvement? The whole approach is unrealistic and evinces a lack of any fundamental appreciation, let alone definitive knowledge, of what constitutes true seaworthiness in a sailing vessel.

Have modern methods *really* improved the overall form of sailing craft, or do we in fact delude ourselves about our progress? *Spray*'s record is not bad, even by today's standards, yet she was probably built in the early nineteenth century. It is doubtful whether any competent naval architect could produce a vessel of the same draft, able to carry the same load, and capable of better performance when sailing with the wind on or abaft the beam—in other words, under the conditions generally met with on long ocean passages. Within such limitations of draft and displacement, our achievement in attaining superior weatherliness might not be as striking as we might expect.

So much, then, for this personal preamble. Suffice it to say that in the *Spray* I found my ideal boat.

5

LINES AND ANALYSIS

Having decided on the *Spray* as *my* boat, I thought the next thing would be to build a model of her. My first attempt at measuring up the small-scale lines in Slocum's book was rather primitive, but to a young chap of nineteen, drawing them out on thick cardboard and cutting the sections for molds seemed marvelous. Unfortunately, what with work at the university and the demands of study, all had to be set aside—but not forgotten. For the next couple of years, the little stack of cardboard templates stayed in a drawer; from time to time, I would steal a loving glance at it before settling back doggedly into my textbooks. Toward the end of my university course, I was able to spare some time to take up again the project of the *Spray*'s lines. I was determined to do it thoroughly, so the rough cardboard sections were discarded and a fresh start made. With limited time, it took about two years in all to complete. The only equipment used consisted of a scale in inches and tenths of inches engraved on the side of a slide rule (an instrument that had seen much use in mathematics exams), and a fine-pointed steel needle. This latter I found greatly facilitated accurate measurement with the scale. The actual process was very slow and much painstaking work was required.

My method was to compare the scale measurement of each and every part of the lines with that of a feature whose actual size was known—for example, the overall length of the boat. With the latter serving as a standard, the former could readily be calculated. The entire set of measurements of the hull lines, heights above and depths below the load water line, and half-breadths from the centerline, were thus calculated with respect to a series of "standards," whose actual measurements were known from the stated general dimensions of the *Spray*. The features of reference I used were length overall, length water-line, and extreme beam. This principle was used throughout the entire investigation, and from the point of accuracy, cannot, I think, be improved upon where small-scale lines are concerned. As a check, several series of measurements were made using a full-size factor for the drawing. This was an average figure obtained from various features of known size and used to convert the measurement of any other feature to its actual measurement by multiplication.

Other methods could of course be used on any similar small-scale drawing lacking an accurate scale line. I suppose an architect would have used proportional dividers or some other instrument, and I know of a few cases where such lines have been "blown up" photographically. At the time, I could think of no other way than the one I used, and I rather think that it has some advantages, which lie in its own drudgery—the very repetition of measurement. By dint of constant remeasurement at different times and by using various standards of comparison, the errors which unavoidably creep into the work are evened out, so to speak, through a statistical average, and the result is probably as accurate as it is possible to get in such cases.

I measured the lines both in Slocum's own book and in his son's biography. The two plans were of different size, and I felt that this would increase the overall accuracy still further. Altogether, eighteen separate tables of offsets were prepared and, finally, an average table, in which each figure was the mean of

27

eighteen different measurements. I drew out this table in pencil on cartridge paper to a scale of one inch to the foot, and prepared another table from the faired lines.

In drawing the lines, several plastic splines were used, each of different thickness according to the type of curve needed. Perspex strips curved beautifully and served as an excellent substitute for the standard wooden drafting splines used by professional designers. Five homemade lead weights were used to keep them in place.

I wanted some idea of the errors involved in all this, both in the actual measurements and the subsequent fairing. Taking the final measured table of offsets as a standard, I determined the difference between its figures and those of the other eighteen tables of which it was an average. The mean divergence from the standard of the total of 1,259 separate values proved to be ⅜ of an inch. In the table prepared from the faired scale drawing, 82 per cent of all individual measurements fell within ¼ of an inch of those in the standard table. So, for my final table of offsets, I would allow approximately ¼ of an inch leeway, as it were, on any one measurement. If this error did exist, it would definitely be cancelled out in the lofting and, in any case, would not affect the accuracy of building a wooden vessel.

The sail plan in both books was measured up in a similar fashion to the lines, except that an average full-size factor was employed for each rather than a direct comparison of every feature with a selected standard. The overall length and waterline length were used to determine this factor. A scale drawing was prepared, ½ inch to a foot, and the final figures on this were all found to be within one inch of those measured in the books. In a sail plan, such an error is negligible.

More recently, I redrew the lines of the *Spray* in India ink on tracing linen, partly to present them in a permanent and reproducible form, and partly because my original pencil lines had all but vanished from constant handling and the additional figuring of an analysis, which will be treated later. The final plans are shown in the Appendix. I consider them as reliable as my amateur methods and primitive equipment would allow. If their accuracy is in any way proportional to the amount of painstaking work which gave them birth, I would have no hesitation in claiming them the best of their kind!

In view of Slocum's remarks about the amazing self-steering ability of the *Spray*, and the fact that many people have doubted his claims, it is surprising that only one naval architect has ever set out to check his assertions in theory, by an analysis of the *Spray*'s lines. The lines of the vessel in *Sailing Alone Around the World* were analyzed by Cipriano Andrade, Jr., an engineer and yacht designer, and the results were published in *Rudder* of December 1908. His article is reprinted in full in the Appendix.

Slocum himself, naturally enough, did not bother about such things. He said: "I did not know the center of effort in her sails, except as it hit me in practice at sea, nor did I care a rope yarn about it. Mathematical calculations, however, are all right in a good boat, and the *Spray* could have stood them." [1] It seemed rather like an open invitation to the architect to step in. There have been many fine designers since Andrade's day, but apparently none thought the old *Spray* worth bothering about. However, a few have commented on Andrade's analysis, some saying it was a lot of rubbish, others that it was a masterly piece of work. It is interesting to have the comments of a modern architect on the subject. Mr. M. D. Lee, of Bijhouwer & Lee, Yacht Designers, New Meadows Boat Yard, Fosters Point, West Bath, Maine, U. S. A., wrote: "In our opinion Mr. Andrade's analysis of the *Spray*'s lines is substantially valid. Perhaps he waxed a bit enthusiastic but she is undoubtedly a fine boat."

After completing my large-scale drawing, I decided to look at several features of the design itself, not only to satisfy my own curiosity about Andrade's work, but also to obtain some further analytical data for comparison with modern yachts. My knowledge of yacht design in general is rather limited and my mathematical ability even more modest, so I concerned myself with only the simpler aspects of the design. With the assistance of several textbooks on the subject, and a small but nonetheless efficient planimeter, I set about analyzing the lines and sail plan. The factors examined were:

1. Thames tonnage
2. Displacement

29

3. Upright and heeled longitudinal centers of buoyancy
4. Hull rise on heeling
5. Weight per inch immersion/emersion at L.W.L.
6. Heeled transverse centers of buoyancy
7. Heeled transverse metacenters
8. Curve of stability
9. Upright transverse center of buoyancy
10. Upright transverse metacenter
11. Metacentric shelf
12. Curve of moments
13. Center of lateral resistance
14. Centers of effort
15. Lead
16. Area of lateral plane immersed
17. Waterline length/beam ratio
18. Speed/length ratio
19. Waterline beam/draft ratio
20. Prismatic coefficient
21. Displacement coefficient
22. Ballast ratio

TONNAGE

The word "ton" is derived from "tun," a cask used in the wine trade, and in former times the size of a ship was estimated by the number of tuns she could carry. Today, small ships are concerned with things other than carrying cargo, and three different kinds of tonnage are in general use. It is still important to know the carrying capacity of a ship, and this is called her net registered tonnage, on which harbor and light dues are charged. The total capacity of the hull in cubic feet is divided by 100 to give the gross tonnage, and the net tonnage calculated from this by making certain deductions for crew's quarters, bosun's stores, engine room, etc. Slocum recorded the *Spray*'s tonnage as being 12.71 tons gross and 9.0 tons net.

The tonnage most commonly used in Great Britain is the Thames Measurement (T.M.), devised in the last century by the Royal Thames Yacht Club as a means of handicapping racing yachts. In calculating the T.M., the only hull factors taken into account are the beam and the length between perpendiculars (L.B.P.). The latter is measured on deck from the fore side of the stem to the after side of the sternpost. The formula used is

$$\frac{(\text{L.B.P.} - \text{Beam}) \times \text{Beam} \times \frac{1}{2}\,\text{Beam}}{94}$$

all the factors being expressed in feet. It can be seen that draft is not considered at all, so that, despite her depth beneath the water, a yacht would have roughly the same T.M. as a raft of the same length and beam. Although this might seem an absurd form of measurement, it serves fairly well for comparing similar types of yachts. However, with craft of widely varying characteristics, T.M. has little practical significance. The American method of describing yachts by their overall length is equally inadequate.

The *Spray*'s T.M. was 21.67 tons.

DISPLACEMENT

The displacement is the total weight of a boat. A floating body displaces its own weight of water, and this can be found by calculating the volume of the underwater part of the hull. The figure, in cubic feet, is then converted to tons and divided by 35, as that is the number of cubic feet of sea water in one ton.

The volume of that part of the hull underwater can be obtained from the lines by two different methods. In one case, the underwater areas of all the body plan sections are determined, and after plotting them to a suitable scale as ordinates spaced the same distance apart as the sections themselves on a line representing the length water line (L.W.L.), a curve of upright areas is drawn out. In the case of the *Spray*, one-fifth scale produced a practical curve, the values being laid off with the scale of the lines, viz., one inch to a foot. The area of this curve, after correction for scale, represents the displacement in cubic feet, and a simple calculation gives the result in tons (see Table 1 and Figure 1). By this method, the *Spray*'s displacement came to 36,034 pounds, or 16.01 tons, excluding the rudder.

In the other case, one finds the areas of the L.W.L. plane and all the waterline planes below it (see Table 3), and draws a vertical displacement curve by plotting these values as ordinates to a vertical axis representing the boat's draft (see Figure 2). These are spaced the same distance as the waterlines of the profile plan, viz., six inches. One-twentieth scale for the ordinates was found to be satisfactory, the values being laid off, as before, one inch to a foot. The area of the vertical displacement curve, after correction for scale, gives the displacement in the same way as for the above-mentioned curve of upright areas. By this method, the figure for the *Spray* was 36,019 pounds.

Considering the errors involved in manipulating a hand planimeter around a drawing, the values obtained by the separate methods are in excellent agreement. Andrade's corresponding figure was 35,658 pounds.

CURVES OF UPRIGHT AND HEELED BUOYANCY

A comparison of the curves of upright and heeled areas is particularly important in any design analysis of sailing craft because of the information gained about hull balance. Using a new waterline inclined at the degree of heel decided upon, the curve of heeled areas is obtained from the lines in a similar way to the curve of upright areas (see Table 2 and Figure 1). The centers of gravity of these curves may be determined by involved mathematical calculations, but a far simpler and equally accurate method is that poising exact paper cut-outs on a knife edge. The point at which the lines of balance intersect the center line, represents the centers of upright and heeled buoyancy, so far as their fore and aft positions are concerned (see Figure 1).

Andrade found the *Spray*'s center of buoyancy (upright) to be exactly at the mid-section. My calculations placed the center of upright buoyancy at 2 inches, and the center of heeled buoyancy, $\frac{5}{16}$ of an inch forward of this section—a separation of 0.14 feet. A close approximation of these centers is usually a criterion of good balance and a characteristic of those craft with harmonizing bows and sterns, for example most Scandinavian and Mediterranean types. Although the bow and stern of the *Spray* look quite different, in profile and in plan, one is immediately struck by the symmetry of her curves of upright and heeled areas. To obtain the latter, I treated the hull as heeled to the deck line, an angle of 14.3 degrees. This would be excessive for the *Spray*, as even close-hauled in a strong breeze she would not go much past 10 degrees. It is amazing that at such an angle of heel her curve still shows almost perfect symmetry—more so, when one realizes that the value of symmetry in both heeled and upright curves has been recognized by designers only quite recently. From the theoretical aspect of buoyancy centers and symmetrical area curves, the *Spray* would thus appear to be well balanced.

HULL RISE ON HEELING

It will be noted that the curve of heeled areas is larger than the curve of upright areas. Most boats have a greater volume of hull above water than below, and because of their general shape, will therefore tend to displace more water on being heeled over by the wind. In other words, when the hull is heeled it should become heavier. This, of course, is impossible, and in fact the whole hull rises somewhat to compensate. Thus the curve already obtained is actually not the true curve of heeled areas. However, the force of the wind that heels the hull will to some extent counteract its tendency to rise and the actual difference between the curves will not be as great as is shown. The factors involved are dynamic ones and far too complex to resolve into any rigid formula. In practice, the curve of heeled areas is thus drawn on the assumption that the hull does not rise. However, the amount of rise is worth investigating for another reason. It depends largely on the character of the midship section, and in particular on the amount of flare, or outward curve of the sides above water. It gives some indication of the relative comfort of a boat in a seaway. Craft with strongly flaring topsides will develop a large lift of hull on heeling, and it is this feature which makes them uncomfortable. On the other hand, a steamer with low bilges and considerable tumble-home, or inward curve of the sides above water, may not rise at all.

The curve of heeled areas for the *Spray* gave a displacement

33

of 38,673 pounds (see Table 2). By a long process of trial and error in raising and lowering the inclined waterline, and evaluating the corresponding displacements, it was found that a hull rise of 1½ inches reduced the total displacement to its original value of 36,072 (including rudder). With such a small rise, the *Spray* would seem to be a comfortable vessel.

WEIGHT PER INCH IMMERSION/EMERSION

The vertical displacement curve mentioned earlier is a very important one. In addition to serving as a check on the displacement, this curve can be used to find the effect of adding or removing weight upon the draft of a vessel. I calculated the weights involved in raising and lowering the *Spray* in the water each inch up to 6 inches either side of the L.W.L. (see Table 4 and Figure 3). Her displacement per inch immersion at the L.W.L. was determined as 1,800 pounds (Andrade's figure was 1,863 pounds), and it therefore requires just over 5 tons to put her down 6 inches. The *Spray* has excellent carrying capacity, and it would take a lot of cargo to make any marked difference to her trim.

CURVE OF STABILITY

One of the most important features of any boat is its stability, as this greatly effects overall safety and seaworthiness. Broadly speaking, stability may be considered as the resistance to pitching and rolling, and is largely dependent upon the shape of the hull. It takes considerably more force to pitch a vessel than to roll it, and longitudinal stability is not often examined in a design. Transverse stability, the resistance to heeling, is a measure of the sail carrying power when close-hauled, and is usually known as "stiffness." In essence, this depends largely on the form of midsection and in particular on the relative positions of the center of gravity (G) and the center of buoyancy (B), and how the latter moves when the boat heels (see Figure 4).

When at rest and in smooth water, a yacht is maintained in equilibrium by two equal and opposite forces, the weight (W) of the yacht acting downwards through G, and the weight of

34

the displaced water acting upwards through B. When she is heeled, G remains unaltered while B moves out to leeward, to a new position B', due to the change in underwater shape. A righting couple, W.GZ, is thus formed which opposes the heeling force and ultimately balances it, unless the form of the vessel is such that she loses all stability and capsizes. W is, of course, constant, so the righting moment is proportional to the length of the lever GZ. The point M is called the metacenter, and the distance from M to G, the metacentric height, which is a measure of the vessel's initial stability.

As a yacht heels, the leeward travel of B increases up to a point where it becomes stationary and begins to recede. The metacentric height also follows suit, reaching a maximum value and then decreasing. Ultimately, in most yachts, there comes a time when M falls below G, the stability changes from positive to negative, and the craft capsizes. In some narrow and deep yachts of the extreme racing type, the amount of ballast is so large and it is placed so low that G is below B. In this case, M can never fall below G, and the yacht has positive stability at all times, even returning to her correct position when upside down in the water. With conventional yachts, however, and in particular the offshore cruiser, considerations of comfort and seaworthiness do not allow such a concentration of heavy weight, and their stability accordingly will become negative on heeling past a certain point. A curve of stability is obtained by plotting righting moment against angle of heel, and its shape depends largely on the shape of the boat's mid-section. Figure 5 shows typical stability curves of the two extremes—the racing machine and the barge—with an intermediate one representing the conventional yacht.

To determine absolute stability values involves calculating the center of gravity, a most laborious process in which the weight and position of each part of the hull, rigging, and gear is taken into account, and an average worked out. Because of its difficulty, it is rarely carried out at all, and any stability figures are generally based on an assumed position of G.

In an early edition of *Yachting Monthly*, T. Harrison Butler described a simple method for obtaining an approximate curve of stability, assuming the stability of the midship section to closely approximate that of the yacht as a whole. By finding the centers of buoyancy at various angles of heel of this section, and the resultant righting levers, a stability curve may be drawn which, if not accurate in absolute unit value, is strictly comparable with the actual curve of the yacht.

In his calculations on the stability of the *Spray*, Andrade assumed the center of gravity to lie on the L.W.L., which he thought was a conservative estimate. I wished to examine the *Spray*'s theoretical stability myself, and felt that Harrison Butler's system could be enlarged to give more accurate values than those obtained using an assumed center of gravity. Instead of taking the mid-section alone, I considered each body section in turn, and calculated the center of buoyancy, metacenter, and righting lever for each 10 degrees of heel up to 90 degrees. Hull rise was allowed for by a corresponding adjustment of the inclined L.W.L. The results, expressed as an average of all the sections, are shown in Table 5. After averaging all the righting levers, a mean righting moment for each angle of heel was calculated, and the results plotted as the curve of stability. This is shown in Figure 6, together with Andrade's curve and the one obtained from the midship section alone.

All show a rather similar form, although actual values differ. On my hull curve, the righting moment is less at all angles of heel than Andrade's, due to his assumed center of gravity being about 7 inches below my calculated mean position. All curves show that the stability becomes zero between 90 and 100 degrees. At this angle of heel, therefore, the *Spray* would capsize and not right herself—in theory at least. In practice, however, the righting moment would be greater at all angles of heel due to the combined effect of ballast in lowering the center of gravity and the trunk cabins in increasing reserve buoyancy. Neither of these was taken into account in my calculations, which thus all err on the safe side.

THE METACENTRIC ANALYSIS

A yacht is said to be well balanced when she has the ability to sail under all reasonable conditions without much helm being necessary for her to hold a straight course. Balance has always been one of the most admired qualities of a yacht and possibly the least understood feature in the whole field of yacht design. In general terms it is the result of a number of air and water forces reaching equilibrium, but the balance is a dynamic one and so subtle that not much definite information is available. The shape of a boat's hull appears to be the most important factor, and in the past, there have been several theories of hull balance. All have been geometrical and static and therein lies their weakness. Today there is no generally accepted system for a comprehensive investigation of yacht balance. Obtaining a close approximation of the centers of upright and heeled buoyancy so that the hull does not alter its fore and aft trim in smooth water is about as far as most architects go in balancing a yacht on the drawing board.

The best-known theory of hull balance is the metacentric shelf system of Admiral Turner. The actual principles behind it are quite complex, and an explanation of why the system works as it does is still obscure. However, despite the questionable nature of the theory, its application by the late T. Harrison Butler in his designs produced boats that were docile on the helm and well balanced. Turner's theory also proved very successful in the field of model racing yachts, so there can be no doubt that he had hit on a fundamental truth.

Essentially, the metacentric theory assumes that balance is due to a symmetrical distribution of buoyancy along the entire length of the hull when heeled. The heeled boat is regarded as "resting" on a plane, known as the metacentric shelf, which is at right angles to the inclined waterline. If the shelf is straight, or winds symmetrically on both sides of its mean axis, the hull rests easily upon it and the boat will probably run straight when heeled. However, if the hull rests when heeled upon an unsymmetrical shelf, motion in a longitudinal direction will tend to make it "slip" to one side or the other, and such a craft will probably carry pronounced weather, or less commonly, lee helm. A metacentric shelf straight and parallel to its axis is the best form, but unusual in any but shallow draft boats. Those forming symmetrical curves, concave or convex according to the type of hull, are also good. An unsymmetrical or "crossed" shelf, approaching the axis at one end and leaving it at the other is usually indicative of poor balance (see Figure 7).

The analysis involves finding first the upright center of buoyancy, by poising an exact paper cut-out of the vertical displacement curve on a knife edge. Where the line of balance cuts the axis is the center of buoyancy (B), considered in a vertical plane. A simple calculation now gives the location of the metacenter (M), the central point for the analysis. The height of M above B is

$$\frac{\text{Sum of cubes of half L.W.L. widths}}{3 \times \text{sum of half areas of upright sections}}$$

A perpendicular from M to the inclined waterline and continued downward across all the sections represents the metacentric axis (M.A.), a section of an inclined plane known as the metacentric plane that passes from stem to stern. The analysis consists in finding out to what extent the volume of the immersed part of the hull is disposed symmetrically with regard to this plane. Figure 8 illustrates the method. Again assuming no rise of hull when heeled, the axis of balance parallel to the M. A. is found for the underwater area of each section along the hull, using the poising technique, and then its distance from the M.A., called the "discrepancy," plotted out along the L.W.L. The resultant curve is the metacentric shelf.

The final stage in the whole analysis is to make a curve of moments. At each body section the discrepancy is multiplied by the corresponding heeled underwater area and the product related to the axis as a curve. This represents the moment of the displacement taken integrally along the entire hull. A symmetrical hull must of course have a symmetrical shelf, and thus a symmetrical curve of moments. For a hull fairly symmetrical in its entirety, that is with symmetrical waterline planes and buttock sections, one might get a shelf and a curve of moments something like those shown in Figure 8. Here the curve of moments winds from windward at the fore end to cross the axis and again return to windward, thus forming three curves, called respectively −A, +B, and −C. Discrepancies to windward are considered minus and those to leeward plus. The moment curve for a crossed shelf has no B curve, simply +A or −A and +C or −C.

Of course, the total windward area must equal the total leeward area, and to obtain this in most cases requires the use of a prometacentric axis. This is drawn close to and parallel with the metacentric axis and is used to calculate another curve of moments having equal windward and leeward areas. The two axes coincide only in the case of those hulls perfectly balanced according to the metacentric system, the so-called "metacentroids." The main value of the moment curve lies in a comparison of the areas of A and C curves. According to the metacentric theory, A should approximate C for proper balance, and certainly never exceed it or the yacht will be hard-headed. For a crossed shelf, where only A and C curves exist, their areas must be equal in any case to satisy the law of hydrostatics. It is therefore useless to compare them and not really necessary, as hulls with a crossed shelf are generally badly balanced.

My calculations placed the upright center of buoyancy 1 foot 1¼ inches below the L.W.L. (see Table 3). The upright transverse metacenter was located 7.86 feet above the upright center of buoyancy and 6.77 feet above the L.W.L. (see Table 6). Assuming (with Andrade) the center of gravity of the *Spray* to lie on the L.W.L., the latter figure thus represents the metacentric height. As mentioned previously, this is a measure of initial stability. In most yachts it is generally several feet, and the value for the *Spray* is exceptionally large.

In view of the *Spray*'s reputed ability as a self-steerer, it is surprising that no one has ever looked at her balance in terms of the modern metacentric system. Probably the tedious nature of the whole process put people off. I spent many long hours working out the *Spray*'s shelf, and the result was rather unusual. I believe that T. Harrison Butler, the eminent English authority on metacentric analysis, once said he thought the *Spray* would have a good shelf in view of her general hull type. Actually, the shelf was a crossed one, yet fairly straight and parallel to the axis for about 62 per cent of its overall length. So in one curve, we have both the worst and the best features of a metacentric shelf. Not being sufficiently expert in the application of the metacentric system, I am unable to draw any definite conclusions from this, though I think the fact of being generally straight and parallel to its axis would count more than crossing it right at one end.

Having a crossed shelf, the curve of moments for the *Spray* showed only −A and +C curves (see Table 7 and Figure 9). As drawn out using the original metacentric axis, the A curve was far larger than the C, and a prometacentric axis had to be used. Its exact position can be found only by trial and error, and I drew out half a dozen, with their respective moment curves, before finding one with equal windward and leeward areas. A prometacentric axis 3 inches to windward of the metacentric axis gave a curve of moments having −A and +C curves of areas 9.36 and 9.64 respectively—close enough for practical purposes. Since the *Spray* has a crossed shelf, the only value of her moment curve is to tell us the distance between the metacentric and prometacentric axes—in this case, 3 inches.

LEAD

Another factor which is of some value in balance considerations is the so-called "lead," which gives an idea of the relation between air and water forces acting on the boat. For practical purposes, the total forces of the water and the wind are assumed to be concentrated at single points on the hull and the sails respectively. Treating the sails and underwater body both as longitudinal planes along the fore-and-aft centerline of the boat, the center of wind pressure is considered to be at the center of gravity of the sail plan, and the center of water pressure at the center of gravity of the underwater profile. These purely geometrical centers, known as the center of effort (C.E.) and the center of lateral resistance (C.L.R.), bear little relation to the actual centers of pressure, which vary constantly as the yacht moves. Since it is not possible to calculate with certainty the positions of these dynamic centers, the geometrical ones are used for convenience and have proved suitable in comparing boats of similar type. In practice, it has been found desirable for proper performance to have the C.E. a little forward of the

C.L.R. The separation of these two centers is known as the lead, and varies with the type of boat, its size, and rig. For comparative purposes, it is expressed as a percentage of the waterline length.

The C.L.R. of the *Spray* was found by poising a paper cut-out of the underwater profile on a knife edge. It proved to be 1.44 feet aft of the mid-section. This compares favorably with Andrade's figure of 1.45 feet.

The centers of effort of the sails were found by the usual geometrical method. These, together with the sail areas, are given in Table 9. The C.E. of the entire sail plan was 1 foot 2½ inches aft of the midship section, or 2.75 inches forward of the C.L.R., thus giving a lead of 0.713 per cent of the waterline length. In theory, such a small lead is generally indicative of good balance.

AREA OF LATERAL PLANE IMMERSED

The area of the immersed lateral plane proved to be 113.74 square feet, with the rudder amounting to 6.7 per cent of this.

WATERLINE LENGTH/BEAM RATIO

This ratio is a valuable one as it greatly influences two important and diametrically opposite factors—stability and speed. Stability demands the greatest possible beam or, alternatively, ballast or a deep keel in a narrow boat, which in many respects is objectionable. Speed demands great length and small beam. The ratio is thus a question of compromise, and the best value is usually accepted as being in the range 2½ to 5. The *Spray*'s figure of 2.27 is thus rather extreme, and the fact that she was also a fast sea vessel is rather unusual. However, there were other and more important features influencing her speed than the above ratio alone.

SPEED/LENGTH RATIO

As a yacht moves forward, she has to push away from her the water displaced by her hull. This takes the form of waves, which vary in shape according to the shape of the yacht. As her speed increases, the waves become more pronounced, and sooner or later every yacht reaches a speed which she cannot exceed under sail due to wave-making resistance. It has been found that there is a relation between this speed and the waterline length of the yacht, usually expressed by the equation

$$\frac{V}{\sqrt{L}} = C$$

where V is the maximum practical speed in knots, and L is the waterline length in feet. However, it is not a simple function of length alone; the type of hull also plays a part, and the speed-to-length ratio represented by the constant C varies according to the hull form. For the full-bodied, short-ended cruiser with rounded rather than flowing lines, the figure might be as low as 1.2; for a large racing yacht, it may reach 1.5. A good modern yacht with easy lines might have a value of about 1.4. The maximum speed of the *Spray* was stated to be 8 knots, thus giving her a constant of 1.42, equal if not slightly better than a good modern type! This is quite astonishing in view of her stumpy ends. However, a study of her diagonals and the clean run of her buttocks will show why she proved so much faster in practice than would ordinarily be expected.

WATERLINE BEAM/DRAFT RATIO

As with the preceding ratio, speed and stability are the two opposing factors to be considered in the waterline beam/draft ratio. The larger its value, the better the initial stability, but because of the increased wetted area and thus frictional resistance, the speed falls off. The value is generally between 1.5 and 2.0. The *Spray*'s value worked out at 3.33, an unusually extreme figure; however, her speed was still good, as we have seen.

PRISMATIC COEFFICIENT

This represents the ratio of a boat's immersed volume, that is, displacement, to the volume of a prism of the same waterline length and maximum sectional area. It thus gives some idea of the fullness of a hull beneath the water, and is rather useful in comparing boats of different types (see Figure 11). The value may vary between 0.5 and 0.7, but usually does not rise above 0.6.

Comparing the mean and maximum immersed cross-sectional areas of the *Spray* gave a prismatic coefficient of 0.65.

DISPLACEMENT COEFFICIENT

It is interesting to assess displacement in relation to the size of a craft, and this is done by means of the displacement coefficient. It provides a handy and useful way of comparing the displacements of different boats. The L.W.L. is taken as the governing dimension, and the displacement related to it by the formula

$$K = \frac{\triangle}{(0.01L)^3}$$

where $\triangle$ is the displacement in tons, L the L.W.L. in feet, and K the required coefficient. By applying this equation to a large number of vessels, it is found that coefficients of the order of 100–250 are characteristic of light displacement craft, a value of about 300 signifies medium displacement, and above 400 is reckoned to be heavy displacement.

The figure for the *Spray* was found to be 488.

BALLAST RATIO

The ballast ratio is given much publicity nowadays due to the large amount of ballast carried by modern yachts. As this is usually in the form of outside ballast, on the keel and immovable, it is important that the amount be accurately decided during the designing stage, so that the yacht will float to her planned waterline. Ballast keels are a relatively modern innovation. Old-time vessels, and particularly those engaged in trading, generally carried their ballast all inside, so that it could be moved to regulate the trim when taking aboard stores and cargo. In those days, such things as ballast ratios were unheard of; any calculations at all were by simple, rule-of-thumb methods. The vessel was trimmed by appearance and by feel. Compared to modern types of craft, these old-timers carried relatively little ballast, relying more on the weight of the cargo and of the hull itself, which was on the whole much more heavily constructed than is the custom today.

The *Spray* was one of this type, and her ballast ratio—the amount of ballast expressed as a percentage of the displacement—is very low by modern standards, 18.63 per cent, compared to the usual 30–40 per cent.

This completes all I have to offer on the design of the *Spray*. It can hardly be said to be complete or even comprehensive. The features I examined are only a very small part of the infinite number of variables which together serve to characterize a vessel and determine her performance. A lot still remains to be done. The field of yacht design is a very extensive one and, as in all other spheres of scientific endeavor, old concepts are being modified, new postulates formulated. I do hope that one day, some competent naval architect will have sufficient interest in the *Spray* to produce a really comprehensive analysis in the light of modern methods.

It will have been apparent that my investigation covered some features of the *Spray* already studied by Andrade, and in most cases, my figures were slightly different. Although my drawing was scaled larger than his—1 inch and ½ inch to the foot respectively—I would not, as an amateur, claim it, or the measurements from it, as any more accurate. No pains were spared in getting and checking the results, but they are certainly not infallible. However, if perhaps not quite so exact or thorough as Andrade's, they represent at least a personal, and so more satisfying, analysis of the old *Spray*.

6

THE SEARCH

Since that day when I bought the little paperbacked edition of *Sailing Alone Around the World*, my interest in the *Spray* has never waned—rather has it become more and more intense; as Arthur Ransome once said: ". . . the desire to build a boat is one of those that cannot be resisted. It begins as a little cloud on a serene horizon. It ends by covering the whole sky so that you can think of nothing else. You must build to regain your freedom." [1]

I was not then in a position to build. Study for a career, lack of funds, and other obstacles combined to make the realization of such a dream a hard and long drawn-out affair. They could not, however, prevent me from making progress on paper. My lines and analysis have already been mentioned; but I decided to look further afield. I began to write.

Since then, I have been trying to track down all available information on the original *Spray* and on the copies and modifications which have been built. Even a little searching soon revealed the fact that readily available data on the *Spray* was rather limited. However, it seemed to me that the actual information which must still be around somewhere would be quite extensive, and I decided to do all I could to find it. This I have been doing ever since. The facts, which one might say are few and far between, make quite an imposing array when they are gathered together; the difficulty lies in collecting them. This necessitates much patient correspondence, and I have written to publishing firms, newspapers, libraries, yachting magazines, yacht clubs, and scores of individuals in many countries in my quest for articles published, photographs of boats and models, details of copies, and comments on their performance. At the time of writing, my files record 602 letters sent out and 525 received—the total correspondence on the *Spray* to date.

Little by little, data came to hand, and eventually more than I dreamed existed; for when I started searching, only one photo of the *Spray* under sail had ever been published, and I had heard of only one copy. This search has been instrumental in putting me in touch with many people, far and wide, directly and indirectly connected with the *Spray* and copies of her. Most, if not all, have been helpful in some way. Letters to the local newspapers brought forth a flood of replies from persons hoping to be of assistance—some with very valuable information, others offering to lend me their prized copies of Slocum's book, and a very few telling me about the time they saw the *Spray* when she was in Sydney. Some had little or no relevant information at all, but were just writing to tell me of their interest in the sea. It made me think that there must indeed be many, many people nursing a secret love for the vast, unfettered freedom of the great oceans, and longing for a little boat, all of their own to sail away for a time from the civilization we boast of, yet which often seems just a little too sophisticated, rather complex, and even monotonous.

To tell the whole story of the search over nine years would take almost another book in itself, but I would like to mention some of the more interesting cases in which little bits of isolated information picked up here and there have resulted in the gradual piecing together of part of the *Spray* story. I have found it a fascinating business, this searching after clues, rather like a detective, letter by letter. Inquiries sometimes seemed to lead to a dead end and then, suddenly, something else cropped up to throw fresh light on the subject and stimulate further research. It can be exasperating at times, too—waiting months, even a year, for replies from correspondents; one may even feel some annoyance when the International Reply Coupons included with all letters still fail to bring forward a response, despite several repetitions by registered mail. It can be frustrating, but, in terms of data collected in the long run and friends made all over the world, it is also very rewarding.

I was amazed how one factor led to another and, by what virtually amounted to a string of coincidences, information was gradually built up.

My first chance contact in the search was with a man in Annapolis, Maryland, whose letter about ocean voyages in small boats I had seen in an issue of *Yachting Monthly* lent to me by a friend. He was also carrying out research, so I decided to write in the hope that he might know something new about the *Spray*. As things turned out, I could not have found a better person to help me, nor a more valuable source of information than Richard Gordon McCloskey. In 1955 he founded The Slocum Society, an international organization which acts as a collecting and distributing center for information on all aspects of pleasure and working boats. Its reference service furthers the interests of boat lovers everywhere; in the years since its inception, the society has become world renowned. Mr. McCloskey is now the honorary secretary of The Slocum Society; his reply was the first bit of outside data I obtained on the *Spray*, and served to stimulate still further inquiry. In this first letter alone, he referred to five copies of the *Spray* which were entirely new to me, and, in the many letters of our subsequent correspondence, he has brought to my notice seven other copies and provided initial data that have enabled me to trace the owners. His clues he calls "grist for your mill," and never is mail more welcome than when that long envelope with blue-and-red checked border and familiar type denotes an airmail note from "Mac."

Not all individuals with whom I have come into contact regarding the *Spray* have been so ready to assist. Some have been downright discouraging in their condemnation of the vessel, and the usual disparaging remarks about "old tubs" and the like become rather irksome with constant repetition. However, the caustic dogmatism of one correspondent indirectly was to put me in touch with the owner of a *Spray* copy recently built. I had written the editor of a yachting journal for information on the *Spray*. In his reply, he recommended that I drop the whole affair; the *Spray* was really a craft to be avoided, and, after all, the "haphazard" way in which she came into Slocum's possession would surely be enough to put me off! This masterly piece of logic was followed by mention of an article in an American magazine about a *Spray* copy. On checking this, I was finally able to locate the builder, Robert Carr of Vermont, who was only too willing to provide further information. His letter, in fact, amounted to fifteen pages, and he even enclosed a copy of his own lofted table of offsets!

In one letter, Mac suggested that I write to Walter Magnes Teller, author of two recent books on Slocum. This I did, and found Mr. Teller a very prolific source of *Spray* material gathered during his many years of research on the captain. From him I was able to obtain many entirely new and unknown photographs of the *Spray*, some under sail, which have given me many pleasant hours of study. He also put me in touch with two people who had sailed on the *Spray* with Slocum, and were able to tell me what they remembered of her performance. There are so few people today who can claim even to have seen the *Spray*, let alone sailed on her, that I considered myself very fortunate in having made such valuable contacts; it seemed to bring me somewhat closer to the old vessel herself.

Mr. Teller also provided a lead that enabled me to trace the owner of a *Spray* copy I had heard of two years earlier. The Mitchell Library in Sydney mentioned an article about the boat in an old issue of *Rudder* magazine. I obtained copies of the article, but could see no way of tracing the owner. Then Mr. Teller happened to mention an advertisement in *Yachting* listing for sale a replica of the *Spray*. A letter to the editor brought a clipping of the advertisement and the good news that my request for information had been forwarded to the brokers concerned, Sparkman & Stephens of New York. This firm replied, giving me the address of the shipyard which had carried out most of the work on the boat in recent years, Cape Cod Marine Service, and suggested I contact them for more information. I wrote, and received by return mail the name and address of the original owner and builder, Captain Robert D. Culler of Massachusetts. Captain Culler proved to be a veritable mine of information on all aspects of the *Spray* and the old coasters of similar type. He had known Victor Slocum intimately and sent me a set of lines of the *Spray* specially prepared for his copy by Victor and Benjamin Aymar Slocum. Culler and I have been corresponding regularly ever since.

It is really astonishing how one stumbles into people who have something to contribute to the overall picture. The first reference I had seen to any *Spray* copy was in Dwight Long's story of his circumnavigation in the ketch *Idle Hour—Sailing All Seas*. One sentence in the last few pages interested me: "Mr. Strout . . . had just completed circling the globe with his wife in a replica of Slocum's *Spray*." [2] The Mitchell Library told me of an article in the *National Geographic* magazine about this voyage and Mac mentioned further articles in *Yachting*. I obtained copies of these articles and of others in *Yachting Monthly*, and tried to trace Mr. Strout for several years with no success. I was about to give up altogether.

One day I was visiting a friend who lives on his yacht in Sydney Harbor. Moored near by was the husky ketch *Little Bear*, on her way around the world. Buzz and June Champion invited us all on board for a marvelous lunch. Of course, we talked nothing but boats the whole time, and I happened to mention my interest in the *Spray*. Buzz surprised me by saying that he had once thought of building her himself, before settling on the *Little Bear*, which was entirely his own work and a fine tribute to his workmanship—one could hardly see a seam in the topsides. The greatest surprise of all was that Buzz knew the very man I had been trying to find for so long—Roger Strout! I wrote him that evening. Mr. Strout told me about the performance of his round-the-world *Igdrasil* in detail and also sent me her lines.

My search for information on the *Pandora*, a copy of the *Spray* built in Perth, West Australia, was one which reached a seemingly dead end and suddenly came to life again. It began, as usual, with a note from Mac giving the brief facts of a voyage to America via the Horn made by this vessel in the early 1900s. He sent me a photo of the *Pandora* in New York Harbor, and this remained all I had on the boat for several more years; despite continuing letters to newspapers and libraries, no one seemed to have even heard of her. One man knew of a steamer of the same name wrecked years ago somewhere in our northern waters, and wondered if this was the boat I was interested in. No, I told him, this was a sailing ship, the first small boat to round Cape Horn. Another wrote that he remembered hearing mention of a boat of that name when he was a small boy in Perth; the name had reminded him of Pandora's box and so stayed in his mind. When he later approached me for a loan of several pounds for a return rail fare to the large country property he claimed to manage, I smelled a rat. Then when he "recognized" the harbor shown in the *Pandora* photo as Perth, my suspicions were confirmed. He didn't get that fare.

I had given up ever finding out more about the *Pandora* when a letter came from a man who had seen one of my published inquiries in the local newspaper. "I read your letter in last Saturday's 'Herald' re *Pandora* and remembered reading about her in an old copy of 'The Rudder' of 1911. I am enclosing the page concerned and hope this may be of some help." It certainly was. Neatly folded within was the yellowed page with a full article about the boat written by a man who had sailed on her in Melbourne. After my encounter with the "con" man, this man's generosity restored my faith in human nature. I thought it might be worthwhile to contact the author of the article, a Mr. Dickson of Geelong, and so wrote to the postmaster there. He replied that this gentleman, who was a chemist, had died, but gave me the address of his son; A. Stanley Dickson said he remembered his father's visit to the *Pandora* but was unable to tell me much more.

However, he thought I might be interested to know that his father had designed and built a boat incorporating the mid-section of the *Spray*. So, in looking for one copy I found another! This vessel, the *Shamrock*, had been sold and he had lost track of it. It had been reported seen in Sydney some years ago but he had not been able to locate it on a recent visit. He sent me several photographs of the vessel and said perhaps I would like to carry on the search.

An inquiry about the *Pandora* to Sydney's leading yachting magazine, *Seacraft*, led me to contact their Perth representative, Jim Sharples, who was able to give me my first real lead on the boat. He told me something of her background and quoted from an old Perth yachting publication which mentioned her being built. The Public Library of New South Wales had no copy of this, but suggested that the West Australian State Library might be able to give me some information. It did, but to the effect that a bound copy of the particular issue I wanted was held by the Royal Perth Yacht Club, and had been mislaid. There was a further note of optimism, however. The library requested more details of my search and said they still might be able to help me. Finally, they gave me the address of Mr. Leslie E. M. Shenton of The Shiplovers' Society. Mr. Shenton made some inquiries for me from Horace Rumble, an old friend of his who, as it happened, remembered the *Pandora* well and, as a boy, often used to visit the boatyard to see her being built. He provided more information on the history of the vessel. Finally, to climax this long quest, I received a letter from George McCarter Jr., the eldest son of the *Pandora*'s builder. A friend of his in Sydney had seen my letter of inquiry in the local newspaper and sent it to him. Being only seven years old at the time the *Pandora* was built, he could not give any details, but nevertheless remembered seeing the boat. He said that his father retired from business through ill health about 1919 and died in 1937.

As far as the *Pandora* was concerned, I had come to the end of the trail. The vessel herself disappeared without trace after leaving New York. What became of her no one will ever know.

In contrast, the search for another "down under" copy of the *Spray* was a most fruitful one, for not only was the boat and her history traced, but I was fortunately able to see her for myself only recently. The first mention of this vessel was in Victor Slocum's biography: "St. Kilda was the home of Mr. Shaw, a genuine *Spray* enthusiast. He got her lines and had a duplicate made by a Melbourne boatbuilder to be preserved in the Antipodes." [3] That is the only published reference to the St. Kilda *Spray* I have seen, and, despite numerous inquiries, no more information came immediately to light. The public libraries in Sydney and Melbourne, although most helpful in the past in providing references, could offer nothing on Mr. Shaw's copy. Then a letter to the *Sydney Morning Herald* started the ball rolling. I received a reply from the son of the builder, now working in Sydney, telling how he and his father worked on the boat. Another letter came from a gentleman who remembered seeing Shaw's *Spray* moored near his former home in Melbourne. He put me in touch with his brother-in-law, a prominent Melbourne boatbuilder, who wrote that this very boat had been lying in his yard for many years. He sent along a photograph and gave me the owner's address. Mr. Johnstone had owned the *Spray* for about twenty years and told me some of her history. Two years later, I went to Melbourne to see him and his *Spray*. Calling at the boatyard, I learned that he had died just a few months earlier and that the vessel had been bought by a Mr. Read. That evening Jack Read rang me at my hotel; in the morning I was to see the very boat I had been searching so long to find. The next day, in warm sunshine unusual for a Melbourne winter, I walked the wide decks of my dream ship. What a joy it was to look over her sturdy, bluff hull, and, going below, see the great roominess of the interior. She was bare of furnishings and the planking had turned gray in ten years of exposure to the weather, but in my mind's eye I saw her rebuilt and rerigged, and, resplendent in new gear and sails, heading out for the open sea. This also was Jack Read's dream, and in the spacious cabin we sat and talked for hours.

My search for a copy of the *Spray* built in England in 1902 was also a most interesting one. The boat's history had a rather international flavor and I had to make inquiries in several countries to obtain information. This vessel was the very first copy

52

ever built, and was afloat even before the old *Spray* herself had vanished from the scene. My first knowledge of her came in a letter from Richard McCloskey, who had been going through old issues of *Yachting Monthly*. In a 1918 issue, mention was made of this English *Spray*, giving a few brief facts about her. This isolated reference was tucked away in my files for further investigation at a later date. I had almost forgotten it when I chanced upon a 1928 issue of the same magazine, and in the correspondence columns found a letter telling how this vessel had been sold abroad to Germany before the First World War. My chances of tracing her now would be pretty slim, I thought. Mac, however, was more optimistic; he suggested writing to the Editor of the German magazine *Die Yacht*. My self-taught and fairly scratchy knowledge of German was then put to work in composing a letter of inquiry. The editor, Herr Gunther Grell, replied that it would be published in a later issue which he would send me, together with any relevant letters received from readers. The result was beyond my greatest expectations. Very soon after, I received a letter from a Herr Leisegang of Hamburg, who had owned the English *Spray* for a number of years. He had renamed her *Heimat*, and in subsequent letters was able to tell me quite a lot about her behavior. Corresponding in German was quite an effort, but the information I obtained was worth it. Herr Wilfried Trapp of Berlin wrote to say that he had the plans of a yacht called the *Spray* which might perhaps be the vessel I was looking for. He sent me the plans and I forwarded a photostat to Herr Leisegang who confirmed that this was indeed the boat. He also told me that he had sold the *Heimat* to Poland before the Second World War. My search was getting more and more involved. The European scene at that time was anything but stable, and I thought I would be very lucky to find out any more. However things were not as bad as they seemed. Out of the blue came a letter from Mac with a copy of a letter written by Wlodzimierz Glowacki, the president of the Polish Yacht Association, to the editor of *Yachting World*, inquiring about the fate of the *Heimat*, and giving some of her history while in Poland. This brought me a little more up to date, and it seemed I was not alone in my search. I wrote to Mr. Glowacki and he told me what he could recall about the vessel. Apparently she had been taken over by the Nazis when they invaded Poland, and that was the last the Poles saw of her. Was this yet another dead end? This time it was Herr Gunther Grell who came to the rescue, sending me a copy of a letter received from Herr Fritz Lescheck of Wedel Holstein who had seen my letter in *Die Yacht*. He knew of a small boat called the *Heimat* which was used by the German Sea Rescue Patrol Service during the war, and had probably been taken to England afterwards as a war prize. It certainly appeared very likely that this was the same vessel, and, if so, what a turn of fate—that this *Spray* should, after half a century, end up in the country of her birth!

I had another letter of inquiry published, this time in *Yachting Monthly*, but no replies were received, so it appeared that none of the world-wide readers of this popular magazine knew anything of the boat. Where next to ask was the big question, and for a time I left it at that. But one day I rang the United Kingdom Information Office in Sydney for a clue. It was suggested that I contact the British Defence Liaison Staff in Canberra, Australian Capital Territory. This I did, and it seemed as if luck was again on my side, for a little later a reply came in from Group Captain F. B. Sutton, who believed that he had crewed in the very boat I was seeking. That was just after the war, and this vessel, a prize from the Germans, had been renamed the *Goldammer* and was at present in Cyprus. He was making further inquiries for me from the R.A.F. station there.

Another English copy of the *Spray* was much easier to trace. I first saw a reference to her while browsing through an old issue of *Yachting Monthly* a friend had given me. In notes for the Bristol Channel District by "N.P.A.," I found the following: "Anyone who has read Captain Slocum's book of his adventures in *Spray* will understand my interest in boarding *Ulula*, of the Portishead Cruising Club. A designed sister ship of *Spray*, she affords one a clear idea of the manliness of the craft that did so much. While she is naturally not as close winded as a finer lined boat, what is lost is made up to her owner in such things as her wonderful headroom, shallow draught for estuary work, and no need of legs for taking hard ground." [4] This was certainly

54

something new. I wrote off at once to the Editor to see if I could contact "N.P.A." He replied that they had lost touch with this correspondent over the years, but gave me the address of the Portishead Cruising Club. The commodore of the club, C. A. Rayner, said that he had sailed on the *Ulula*, and sent some fine photographs of her under sail. He also gave me the name and address of the last English owner. A year went by; I had almost given up hope of hearing from him when a reply came in. He had been ill for a long time and unable to attend to correspondence. In several letters, he told me all he remembered about the history of the vessel and her performance. The boat now is owned by an officer in the Irish Navy, but repeated attempts to contact him have been unsuccessful.

In his book *Kurun Around the World*, Jacques-Yves le Toumelin refers to a *Spray* copy he saw at the Balboa Yacht Club. "*Sagamore* with her cutwater had immediately caught my eye, and I was pleased when I had an opportunity to see her at close quarters. I even saw her out of the water. The plans for her building had been inspired by the famous *Spray*, belonging to that amazing seaman Slocum." [5] I wrote to the Balboa Yacht Club who were able to give me the name and address of *Sagamore*'s owner. After some time I received a reply from him, telling about his work in refitting the boat and giving some details of her behavior. The *Sagamore*, he said, was a modification of the *Spray* designed by John Hanna. I had heard of this design before, which Hanna called the *Foam*, but, until then, had never been able to trace any of the many vessels built to it.

Only recently luck came my way again, with another *Foam*—in fact, the first one ever built. This case was unique in the entire search, for the owner himself got in touch with me first! It was a pleasant change from the usual long line of letters that has laboriously traced many another copy. This vessel was built as the *Foam* but has changed names and owners a number of times since. Now named the *Island Trader*, she is owned by Horace Schmahl of New York. A friend had passed on to him an article I had written on the *Spray* some years previously, and he said he thought I might be interested in hearing about his copy. I certainly was, for she is a truly magnificent vessel, maintained in first-class condition, and is the only schooner-rigged copy I have come across. In several letters, Mr. Schmahl gave the complete history of the boat, after much research on his part, and sent along many excellent photographs of her, including one in color. He gave me a detailed account of her performance and was able to obtain the lines and a table of offsets from one of the early owners of the vessel. The *Island Trader* is presently on a voyage around the world, and I am looking forward to meeting Mr. Schmahl and his family when they arrive in Australia.

It was in an excellent roundup of *Spray* material in *The Spray* (*Journal of The Slocum Society*) some years ago that I first saw a reference to a copy built at Bangkok. As far as I know this was the only *Spray* ever built in Asia, and so far all my attempts to trace it have been unsuccessful. In his book *Macpherson's Voyages*, Macpherson mentions seeing this boat in Dobo, in the Aroe Islands. He died some years ago, but with McCloskey's help I was able to contact Macpherson's constant sailing mate, Bill Leng, in England. He was with Macpherson when they saw the Dobo *Spray*, which was then owned by the Celebes Trading Company, and told me what he remembered. For further information, I got in touch with the Netherlands Consul in Sydney, who wrote that the Aroe Islands were now in Indonesian territory. The Indonesian Embassy was unable to help, but suggested writing to the Department of Sea Communications in Djakarta. After a considerable time, I received a reply from the Australian Embassy in Djakarta. "The Department of Sea Communications of the Government of The Republic of Indonesia have spoken with me concerning your letter of 25th January 1960. They regret that they are unable to help you in any way with information on the supply cutter *Spray*, as personnel from 1938—in the days of the Netherlands East Indies—have all been changed. Nor would there be any records. They have also informed me that they are unaware of any trading company operating in those islands at the time you mention."

It occurred to me that the trading company which owned the *Spray* may have been Dutch owned, so I wrote again to the Netherlands Consul. He replied: ". . . judging by general circumstances in the pre-war Netherlands Indies, it is most unlikely that a small sailing craft as you refer to was owned by a Netherlands Company. It is quite possible that it was owned and operated by local indigenous groups. It is regretted therefore that I cannot offer you any information that will enable you to trace the owners."

It seemed that I was back again where I started. However I still have hopes of finding out more about the boat, this time from Bangkok, where she was built. One never knows.

These are just a few examples of the many coincidental threads whose discovery and weaving together over the years has proved a most interesting task. Research is still continuing as new facts come to light, and I am always on the lookout for more information. Only when one becomes really involved in this investigation does one realize just how much of the *Spray* story remains to be told. Loose threads, unsolved mysteries—fresh horizons these, that beckon and lure the wanderer on.

ORIGINS

The origin of the *Spray* is shrouded in mystery. She was a very old craft even when Slocum found her, and no one knew then exactly when or where she was built. Slocum wrote:

The *Spray*, as I sailed her, was entirely a new boat, built over from a sloop which bore the same name, and which, tradition said, had first served as an oysterman, about a hundred years ago, on the coast of Delaware. There was no record in the custom-house of where she was built. She was once owned at Noank, Connecticut, afterward in New Bedford and when Captain Eben Pierce presented her to me, at the end of her natural life, she stood . . . propped up in a field at Fairhaven. Her lines were supposed to be those of a North Sea fisherman. In rebuilding timber by timber and plank by plank, I added to her freeboard twelve inches amidships, eighteen inches forward, and fourteen inches aft, thereby increasing her sheer, and making her, as I thought, a better deepwater ship.[1]

Victor Slocum said that the *Spray* had been a swordfisherman, while owned at Noank and New Bedford.[2]

58

The original vessel had a centerboard, according to Victor Slocum, but, strangely enough, the Captain himself made no mention of this. A common practice with many small American coasters was the centerboard passing through the garboard alongside the keel, and the old *Spray* probably followed this. Slocum, however, omitted it entirely, knowing it would be a source of weakness on a long ocean cruise, and deepened the outside keel.

Most yachtsmen today tend to think of the *Spray* as an extreme and unusual type of boat. This is true now and was so even when Slocum rebuilt her, but the fact is that her model, although uncommon as a yacht, was formerly one of the most popular in the United States for small working vessels.

In his book *American Small Sailing Craft*, Howard I. Chapelle gives the plans of a boat that bears a striking resemblance to the *Spray*. It was a type of small working sloop once popular in Long Island Sound and eastward to Cape Cod, and had been developed from the New York sloop. Mr. Chapelle wrote:

The most important of the sloop-rigged small-boat types used in the fisheries was the New York sloop, which had a style of hull and rig that influenced the design of both yachts and workboats for over thirty years. The New York boats were developed sometime in the 1830s, when the centerboard had been accepted. The boats were built all about New York Bay, particularly on the Jersey Shore. The model spread rapidly, and, by the end of the Civil War, the shoal centerboard sloop of the New York style had appeared all along the shores of western Long Island Sound, in northern New Jersey, and from thence southward into Delaware and Chesapeake waters. In the postwar growth of the southern fisheries, during the 1870s and 80s, this class of sloop was adopted all along the coasts of the South Atlantic states and in the Gulf of Mexico; finally, the boats appeared at San Francisco. The model did not become very popular, however, east of Cape Cod.

The New York sloop was a distinctive boat—a wide, shoal centerboarder with a rather wide, square stern and a good deal of deadrise, the midsection being a wide, shallow V with a high bilge. The working sloops usually had a rather hard bilge. . . .

An adaptation of the New York sloop model to the requirements of the fisheries in more exposed waters is illustrated in the small sloops once built in the boatshops at Noank, Connecticut, and other towns along the Long Island Sound shores, and in Narragansett Bay. These working-sloops were intended for tonging and dredging oysters, lobstering, and line fishing. In general, they were relatively deeper and heavier than the old New York sloops and the cats. They carried more ballast and were less heavily rigged, as befitted their employment in waters subject to severe squalls and storms, even in summer. . . . The Noank style of centerboarder illustrates one of the best of the centerboard sloop models in the fisheries, where rough water and strong winds were to be met.[3]

Mr. Chapelle believed that the *Spray* was one of this type. In a letter, he said:

Spray was nothing more than a very common fishing sloop used on Long Island Sound. This type was *not* built as early as 1800, it came into existence in the 1830s–'40s and by the late '50s was in use all along the Atlantic seaboard of the U. S. The type can still be seen—two sloops at Cambridge, Maryland, and at least six are in existence on Long Island Sound and Great South Bay, I believe. These sloops were most common in the oyster fisheries. The centerboard sloops, particularly after 1845, often resembled the *Spray* plans, some at least were as full forward and as fine aft as she—others were much sharper. The surviving oyster sloops are very close to *Spray* plans except they have centerboards.

Mr. Chapelle added that the Bridgeport sloops were even closer to the *Spray* model than the Noank type.

It is interesting to have a consenting opinion from the other side of the Atlantic. In reply to my inquiry requesting information on the origin of the *Spray*'s lines, the English naval architect John Leather wrote:

Capt. Slocum's famous *Spray* was, from her lines, arrangement, and original rig, nothing more than a rebuilt Delaware oyster sloop of a type long used in dredging the extensive Delaware Bay fisheries. These were characterized by their full-bowed, beamy and shallow hulls; with tumbled quarters, low freeboard and tucked-up counters; fiddle heads and sloop rigs having the mast stepped in the eyes. The great beam not only gave initial stability and carrying capacity on a limited draught, but also afforded necessary deck space for hauling dredges and sorting or carrying oysters.

The type seems to have developed from the shallops of Colonial times, which were small chubby-bowed fishing and coasting craft built by the shipwright sent out with the early settlers. Gradual local evolution led to the sloop rig, as in *Spray*, but some time during the nineteenth century most adopted the schooner rig due to the gradual increase in size, which grew to around 70 ft. by the 1920s, when numbers of them were still being built for the fisheries whose laws forbade power dredging until 1945. Since then all rigs have been cut down and wheelhouses shipped; though the graceful hulls still show the same form as *Spray*.

Similar sloops were also used on the Maine Coast and on Chesapeake Bay, where they were largely superseded by bugeyes and, later, skipjacks, which still work the Maryland grounds under sail.[4]

Although, as Mr. Leather says, the shallops of Colonial times probably were the ancestors of the *Spray* type, Slocum's statement that her lines were supposed to be those of a North Sea fisherman may not be so far from the truth. The boats of the early American colonies were without doubt based on European models, and in hull form resembled medieval trading vessels. Although the heavy influx of immigrants in large national groups did not begin until the 1830s, and hence foreign types of small craft did not appear as distinct models and rigs until after this date, individual shipwrights from England, France, Holland, and Scandinavia did go out with the early settlers and carry on their art in the New World. It may have been one of these who, sometime in the late eighteenth century, built a vessel—perhaps even the *Spray* herself—on the lines of some sturdy North Sea fishing boat well known to him in his own country, thereby establishing a model which proved so efficient and suitable for its purpose that it held sway for the best part of a century.

Those who think of the *Spray* as a "freak" boat forget that her type was, and in many cases still is, very common among fishing and work boats generally in many parts of the world.

61

The suitability of a sturdy, bluff-bowed, beamy, and shallow hull for a working boat model appears to have been well recognized by fishermen and traders of many lands, and it is surprising how many such vessels are like the *Spray* type. These craft are doubtless the result of an empirical and independent evolution down through the centuries.

Whether or not Slocum was correct about the *Spray*'s North Sea ancestry, some North Sea fishing craft of today still possess many of her features. This may well be purely coincidental and have no bearing on her origin, but it is nonetheless interesting.

French sardine luggers, for example, all show the same very broad beam and shoal draft; a fleet of sturdy luggers from the River Cauche in France, built for trawling in the North Sea and the Channel, and formerly often seen at work off the Thames and the Kentish coast, all greatly resembled the *Spray*. One of these vessels was bought by an Englishman, who wrote about her in *Yachting Monthly*. He said:

For some time I have owned and sailed a vessel (I dare not call her a yacht) which, though not built to the lines of *Spray*, is apparently identical in dimensions, form, and proportions. She is 38 ft. over all, 33 ft. on the water line and 14 ft. 2 in. beam. She has the same cod head and mackerel tail as *Spray*, and as will be seen from the accompanying photograph, the same type of section. Comparing the two, the only difference that I can see lies in the stern. *Spray* has a very short counter. My boat has a well raked transom, which amounts to nearly the same thing. The draught is 4 ft. 6 in., and I have the same headroom under deck, with 6 ft. clear under deckhouse. . . . Although built as recently as 1920, she is one of a type that I firmly believe has continued unchanged for a century or more, built to moulds that have been handed from father to son. . . .[5]

The French luggers from St. Valery-sur-Somme also had a form very reminiscent of the *Spray*, but they were two-masted craft. Most yachtsmen are rather horrified by the *Spray*'s huge beam, her overall length to beam ratio being 2.6, but some of the fishing boats on the west coast of France have only two beams or less to their length!

The English yachtsman James Wharram, while cruising on the northwest coast of Spain in his catamaran *Tangaroa*, noted a *Spray* likeness in the timber-carrying gaff sloops of that region. He commented: "The next morning I examined several of the sloops. They were, measurement for measurement, exactly the same as Slocum's *Spray* before he rebuilt her." [6]

Some types of Scandinavian working craft, in particular the Danish and Norwegian trading ketches, had the full bow, shoal draft, and wide beam carried right aft to a large square transom, similar to the *Spray*. Much the same features are apparent on the 35-foot cutter *Sol-Lys*, owned and designed by the well-known Danish naval architect, the late Knud E. Hansen, on the lines of the Baltic trading cutters of the past century. She was fully described in the November 1958 *Yachting Monthly*.

In the biography of his father, Victor Slocum wrote of the *Spray:* "On a smaller scale she greatly resembled Amundsen's exploring ship *Gjøa*, which he said was a Norwegian herring boat before he took her through the Northwest Passage. The writer saw the *Gjøa* blocked up in Golden Gate Park, San Francisco, where she may be seen at the present day; the resemblance of the *Spray* to the *Gjøa* was very striking, particularly in the apple bow and broad square stern." [7]

Many of the Estonian coastal schooners formerly engaged in the timber trade were also quite similar in appearance to the *Spray*.

The British working vessels have generally been far deeper and less beamy than the *Spray*, though some have shown a superficial resemblance. The bawley of the Thames Estuary was a typically beamy, shallow vessel with a finer bow than the *Spray* type. The luggers of the southeast coast of England had a rather similar form, although much deeper and flatter in the floor. These were beach craft, and while their clinker construction was a heritage of Norse ancestry, the hull form is reminiscent of Dutch fishing vessels.

Much further afield, boats can still be found quite like the *Spray*. I have a photograph that was taken in Buenos Aires Harbor in 1926, and several fishing craft shown there could well be sister ships to the old *Spray*, so closely do they resemble her.

The old boat certainly appears to have had many relatives in various parts of the world. But in spite of its popularity with fishermen, the *Spray* type is hardly the ideal of modern yachtsmen. Their standards, however, seem to be based more on rating rules and social prestige than on fundamental concepts of seaworthiness or comfort. With working vessels, the position was completely different. Their owners' livelihood depended on their ability to keep at sea in all reasonable weather without failure of hull, rig, or gear. Strength and simplicity were the essential features, and utility of far greater importance than mere fashionable appearance. Down through the ages it bred a very sturdy type of vessel, and on her world voyage the *Spray* proved her type not one whit less suitable for ocean cruising than it was for coastal fishing.

8

THE MOWER STORY

For a long time, there has been some doubt about the authenticity of the *Spray*'s lines published in the captain's book.
Indeed, the subject has aroused as much controversy as the
design itself. Slocum wrote: "I gladly produce the lines of
the *Spray*. . . . No pains have been spared to give them accurately. The *Spray* was taken from New York to Bridgeport,
Connecticut, and, under the supervision of the Park City Yacht
Club, was hauled out of water and very carefully measured
in every way to secure a satisfactory result. Captain Robins
produced the model." [1] The secretary of The Slocum Society,
Richard Gordon McCloskey, went to Bridgeport in 1954 to
try to obtain more information and check on Slocum's assertions. He found that the Park City Yacht Club was organized
in 1888 and went into oblivion in 1934; he was unable to find
any of its records or any survivors who knew about it.

Slocum's statement implies that the published lines were the
direct result of the Bridgeport measurement, and his reference
to a model seems merely an afterthought. However, when one

65

reads Slocum's letters to his publishers, The Century Company, the model becomes more important. This correspondence remained unknown until discovered by Walter Magnes Teller in the course of his research on the Captain. In 1899, in one letter, Slocum spoke of "measuring aloft." In another, he said: "The *Spray* is to be hauled out Sat at Capt Robins Yard Bridgeport—Capt Robins is prepareing a model of her—Mr Mower, designing Editor, Rudder is engaged to draw the line—I am looking, carefully, over the whole of it and will tumble it in very soon." In a later letter, Slocum wrote: "I daresay you wonder what has come of *Spray* model etc but your heart will soften when you see the very exact model I leave with tonight—scale one inch to the foot—It is a poem! It is the certified work of a professional or master moddler and I blead over it myself besides—I take it first to the Rudder designers to transfer the lines onto paper." [Spelling as original.]

That comment would seem to indicate that the published lines were not taken from the actual boat at all, but from the model. However, the lines were signed "C. D. Mower," and one naturally wonders what part he played in the affair. The mystery is partly cleared up by Thomas Fleming Day, who, in an article about Slocum in *Rudder* magazine, said: ". . . he brought in the model of *Spray* and Mr. Mower took off the lines as they appear in his book." [2] That would seem to settle the question of the origin of the lines, but there is still the doubtful point of their accuracy. Slocum's statements in his book and his letters leave no doubt at all that he himself believed the measurements to be completely accurate. His son was also convinced of this, and Captain Culler of the Oxford *Spray*, who knew Victor Slocum personally, said that he "showed no doubt as to the lines being authentic." One of Victor Slocum's closest friends was Mr. Eric Squires, who told me,

Victor Slocum and I met for the first time during 1942, when we were working for the United Fruit Company. An immediate friendship sprang up that was to continue without interruption to 1949 when Victor died. . . . Victor knew of the model, but it was our joint opinion that the lines shown in the book are the result of direct measurements, because this was the very reason for the haulout. The issue of the model only clouds the picture. It is hard to believe that the men responsible for the measurements and subsequent plans would be guilty of such unprofessional conduct, as to take the lines from a model, when the actual vessel was available. The plans shown in the book are as authentic as could be. Victor and Ben [Benjamin Aymar Slocum] extracted these plans from the book as others have, including me. As *Spray* was around for several more years after her measurement, Captain Slocum was aware of the importance of the dimensions by this time. If the Park City Yacht Club dimensions were in error, Joshua would have corrected them. The fact that this was not done, speaks for itself.

This is certainly what one would assume from Slocum's statements alone; however, there is some evidence that the model was not as exact as Slocum thought. I have heard this from several people, but have only seen one published reference to it. In the American magazine *Yachting*, there was a review of Victor Slocum's biography of his father by "C. H. H.," who made mention of the supposed measurement of the *Spray* by Mower as ". . . a joke to any who ever heard that careful naval architect spin the yarn of that alleged process." [3] A letter to *Yachting* revealed "C. H. H." to be Charles H. Hall, who was associate editor of that magazine when he wrote this review. The editor wrote me: "The question of Mower's having taken off the lines of the *Spray* was a matter of Mr. Hall's personal knowledge, gained from conversations he had with Mr. Mower." Unfortunately, Mr. Hall died some years ago, and that would seem to close this little avenue of investigation.

The well-known American naval architect and author Howard I. Chapelle recently clarified the entire issue. In a letter to Richard Gordon McCloskey, he said:

To begin with, as an apprentice draftsman I was once employed by Charles D. Mower, Naval Architect. This was in 1919. Charles Mower had once been naval architect for *Rudder* magazine and there he drew the plans of the *Spray* that Slocum published.

Mr. Mower told me the following story, as well as I can remember it. One day Thomas Day and Captain Slocum came into the room Mower used and Day told him that he wanted him, Mower, to take off the lines of the *Spray*. Mower and Slocum then went to the boatyard—on City Island perhaps—and there Mower found the *Spray* afloat. He told Slocum he could not take off the lines of the boat afloat but he would measure her above the water—profile, deck plan, rig, etc.—and that when the *Spray* was hauled on the marine railway to let him, Mower, know and then he would measure up the hull. Mower and Slocum measured what they could and Mower returned to his office and reported to Day. What had been measured was drawn up and laid aside.

Some time passed and then, one day, Slocum came in with a half-model of the *Spray*. Mower asked him if this was the building model. Slocum said no, it was a model made by the boat yard operator where *Spray* had been hauled up and that he had helped the boat yard operator measure the hull. Mower assumed they had taken off the lines to make the model. But upon applying the model's lines to the measurements made afloat, Mower found many discrepancies and, Slocum not being available, he finally visited the boat yard. Upon inquiry the yard owner told him they had not actually taken off the lines but had taken some measurements and made the model by eye.

Due to the time lost, and a promise Day had made that the plans would be published, Day instructed Mower to work up the plans as best he could and the result was published as the drawings of the *Spray*.

Mower felt badly about this as he knew many people had accepted the plans as the accurate record of the *Spray*. While the drawings were "close" to what the hull was they were not accurate enough to justify the Andrade analysis that appeared in *Rudder*. . . .

The story made a strong impression on me as I was interested in *Spray* and Slocum and that is how I came to discuss it with Mower. Charles Mower was a very capable and reliable man; I would accept anything of this nature he told me with utmost confidence.

The late Charles Hall, of Yachting, knew this story as he asked me once if I had heard it, so probably Mower told it to others. I am sure Slocum thought the boat builder's half-model was accurate enough but the evidence Mower had, in making drawings, showed that the model was not accurate and in fact was only an approximation.

Chapelle commented further: "Taking off is hard to do unless you have had experience and the proper equipment. I would naturally suspect any boat yard job of this kind. . . . I have taken off a great many lines of boats and I know that if I had been in Mower's position I would not have accepted the half-model as correct."

It is beside the point now to blame anyone for the nature of the *Spray*'s lines as published; however, one cannot but feel that it was rather unfortunate that circumstances did not permit her lines to be taken off. It may come as a shock to many *Spray* enthusiasts that the lines in Slocum's book are not exact, and that all "copies" of the boat based on them can be only approximations. However, even if Mower's lines are not absolutely correct, they certainly reflect the general shape and type of the *Spray*. Divergencies of measurement that might horrify a naval architect, accustomed to working in sixteenths of an inch, are purely of academic interest and of little practical significance as far as her bluff hull is concerned. The lines have proved close enough in practice for copies of the *Spray* to duplicate her performance, and that is surely the main thing. One owner of an American copy said: "Whether they are the true lines of the *Spray* or not, we will never know, but if they turn out a boat that has all of the features ascribed to the *Spray*, who cares?"

Many years ago, the English magazine *Yachting Monthly* published a design under the heading "Lines of *Spray*—Capt. Slocum's famous ship" with this note: "Following the recent correspondence in our columns on Capt. Slocum's famous *Spray*, we reproduce above, through the courtesy of 'Le Yacht,' lines said to be of this vessel, drawn up by M. Arnould Moreaux, a French naval architect." [4] I contacted the editor of *Le Yacht*, who wrote that M. Moreaux had never seen the true plans but prepared his lines in 1924, after reading descriptions of the boat. A French edition of Slocum's book was not published until 1936, so probably M. Moreaux grew tired of waiting and decided to do his best with the boat's general measurements.

I measured the small-scale lines, prepared a table of offsets, and compared the figures to those from the published lines of the *Spray*. The maximum difference was six inches, with the average only a little over two inches. For a drawing which was probably based only on the *Spray*'s principal dimensions, such close agreement with Mower's lines is quite remarkable. This seems to illustrate the rather uncritical nature of the *Spray* model, and also, as a corollary, might give some idea of the general accuracy of the Bridgeport model. If a man, having only the *Spray*'s main "statistics" and some general descriptions of the boat from which to work, can produce lines well within say, six inches of error, surely an experienced boatyard operator and, according to Slocum, "expert" modeler, with the actual vessel herself to study, could make a model with at least this degree of approximation. Captain Robins' model, and the lines Mower prepared from it and his own measurements of the *Spray*, were probably accurate to within a few inches. This is, I think, a fairly conservative estimate.

Since the published lines are approximate only, it should be emphasized that the analysis in Chapter 5 and in the Appendix are, of necessity, purely indicative, and by no means absolute as far as the *Spray* is concerned. However, regardless of how close to the real vessel the lines were, the fact remains that they themselves represent a fairly worthwhile type, and have been used for so many copies that an accurate mathematical appraisal is justified.

9

MODELS AND PICTURES

One of the most interesting features of the search for *Spray* material was the discovery that there were a number of models of her in existence, made by people who wanted to see her in three-dimensional miniature. The best model I have come across was made by Slocum's youngest son, Benjamin Aymar Slocum, and presented by him to the Peabody Museum, Salem, Massachusetts. A photograph of this appears in Victor Slocum's biography. I wrote to the museum and was sent two prints of the little *Spray*. It is a fully rigged, whole hull model, and is so accurate that one can almost imagine one is looking at the original boat.

One of my letters of inquiry on the St. Kilda *Spray*, published in the *Sydney Morning Herald* several years ago, obtained for me my own little replica of the *Spray*. I received a reply from John B. Walker, ship modeler, of Melbourne, telling of a fully rigged, waterline model of the *Spray*, scaled ½ inch to the foot, which he constructed many years ago on the basis of data obtained from the Peabody Museum. It was built for a man named Smith who wanted a copy of the *Spray* but died of fever in New Guinea during the war. Mr. Walker also made him a larger model of the hull only, constructed like a full-size boat, so he could design his interior layout. This model he paid for and took away. What became of it is another unsolved *Spray* mystery. The rigged model, however, was located, and I purchased it on a visit to Melbourne some years ago. It stands in its glass case behind me as I write, and I have spent many an evening studying it, noting every aspect of hull, rig, and gear. One day, I hope to have it on the cabin bulkhead of my own copy of the *Spray*.

Tracking down *Spray* models is interesting enough in itself, but it could prove useful in another way. In view of the doubtful authenticity of Mower's lines, finding a model which had been made from measurements taken off the *Spray* herself would prove invaluable in settling the controversy about their accuracy. Of course, it is very unlikely that the Bridgeport model will ever be located now, but there could still be others.

One model which might fall into this category has so far eluded my search. A photograph of it appeared in a 1918 issue of *Yachting Monthly*, with a letter from T. A. Dickson which said: "While Slocum stayed at Launceston, Tasmania, another 'old sea dog' made a model of *Spray* which has since come into my hands. I enclose a photograph which I have had taken of this model, and hope it may prove of interest to admirers of the Grand Old Man who loved our glorious heritage—the sea—and did a thing well 'for its own sake'." [1]

The *Spray* lay on a beach alongside a jetty at Launceston for about a week while Slocum journeyed around the neighboring countryside to refresh himself for the rest of his voyage. She was set there on an unusually high tide, and had very little water around her. There would have been ample opportunity for anyone interested to have examined her thoroughly and even measured her up for the model. Slocum merely records that she had plenty of visitors during this time. The model itself appears to be about ¼ inch to the foot. The name T. A. Dickson seemed familiar, and I suddenly remembered that this was the same man who had sailed on the *Pandora* and written about it in *Rudder* magazine.

In my letter to Mr. Dickson's son I asked about this model, and he replied: "The model of the *Spray* I remember very well, and the delay in answering your letter has mainly been brought about by time spent in trying to locate it, which unfortunately I have been unable to do. I remember it until the late 20s, but cannot trace it since then."

In looking for another model of the *Spray*, I was spurred on by an assertion that it had been taken off the original boat. In one issue of *The Spray* there was reference to a half-model hanging in the headquarters of the Cruising Association, Baker Street, London.[2] I wrote to this body for details and the secretary replied that the model was made by B. S. Woolacott of New Zealand and had been presented to the Association by Dr. H. Nockolds of London. The inscription below the model stated:"This model is taken off the original *Spray*. . . ." At last, it seemed, I was on the track of something interesting. I managed to contact Dr. Nockolds, who said that he found the model aboard the 8-ton cutter *Juno* which he bought from Woolacott in 1922. He believed that this gentleman had gone to New Zealand, and said that Eric Hiscock, in his book *Around the World in "Wanderer III,"* had referred to a Woolacott who designed New Zealand cruising yachts. Two yacht clubs in New Zealand gave me Mr. Woolacott's address and I wrote to him. He recalled making the model, and said it was based on the lines held by Victor Slocum and not "taken off" the *Spray* at all. The inscription, which had aroused hopes of settling the *Spray* controversy, was thus in error.

One of the most unusual models of the *Spray* was made by A. G. Law of New York. His miniature work truly shows all the care and precision typical of a modern watch. Mr. Law tells his own story:

Under separate wrapper I am sending a photograph of my little yawl, *Spray*, along with some other material which will explain what I have been attempting to do over a period of many years.

73

My little ships are not 'ship models,' in spite of what most viewers, for want of a better and more descriptive name, usually refer to them. Mine are miniature museum pieces of maritime fine art—"maritime sculptures" if you will. They are all water-line ships, mounted upon hand drawn maps, in my own workmanship and design of cases, and in extreme miniature size. . . . In presenting my work I have tried to combine the little ships with cartography, bibliography, jeweller's precision workmanship, design, lore of the sea, historical accuracy, and many hours of research. . . . The plans for my little *Spray* (it measures only 4½ inches at the waterline) were taken by photostat from a first edition of Capt. Slocum's book. It is only slightly larger than the printed plans in Slocum's book.

There have been several paintings of the *Spray*. The best I have seen was reproduced in color on the dust cover of Victor's biography of his father—the Sheridan House edition—which was given to me by Benjamin Aymar Slocum. This painting was by the well-known marine artist, Charles Rosner, and is so accurate that it could well be a photograph. It shows the *Spray* bowling along in a quartering wind, with all working canvas set, and a curl of white water at her bow. The Stars and Stripes flies bravely from the mizzen truck, and Slocum stands at the wheel. The contrast of white foam on the deep blue water, the swelling curve of the sails against a straw-colored sky, makes a truly delightful picture.

In 1944, a nephew of Joshua Slocum, Commodore George Slocum of Detroit, Michigan, approached the late President Franklin D. Roosevelt to have one of the Liberty ships named after the famous captain. The suggestion was agreed to, and on December 15, 1944, the S.S. *Joshua Slocum* was launched at Portland, Maine. Commodore Slocum and his wife presented an oil painting of the *Spray* to be hung in the wardroom of the new Liberty ship. This painting, by Benjamin Turner Stephenson, one of America's best known contemporary marine artists, is not as striking as the one by Charles Rosner, nor is it so accurate in portraying the character of the *Spray's* hull.

When I began research on the *Spray* in 1954, only one

photograph of the vessel under sail was generally known to exist. Through his two recent books on Slocum, Walter Magnes Teller has done much to arouse public interest in the captain and his boat, and as a result of his efforts, more material has come to light, including many hitherto unpublished photographs of the *Spray*.

Wherever Slocum went, the *Spray* attracted much attention, and there must have been many photographs taken of the old vessel on her voyage around the world. No doubt quite a few still exist, lying unnoticed in family albums with other heirlooms from the past. A photograph of the *Spray*, taken while she was at St. Helena, was mentioned by Frank A Wightman in his book *The Wind Is Free*. He said, "In wandering round the village the day after we arrived, we went into the island chemist's, and there we met Mr. Warren, who has been on the island since he was a lad and is a reference library of island history. We spent hours looking through photographs of ships that are now only famous names. . . . A photograph of Captain Slocum sitting on the deck of the *Spray*. How many people have seen a photograph of the *Spray!* It must have been taken before the beginning of this century." [3]

I got in touch with Mr. Warren who, at the time of writing to me, was eighty-five years old. He remembered the photo, but thought that it must have been sold with his business some years ago.

My own local search for photographs met with some success. An appeal in the press brought forth a letter from Slocum's niece by marriage, Mrs. Dulcie Kane of Sydney. She is the daughter of George Washington Walker, whose sister, Virginia, Slocum married in Sydney in 1871. She mentioned a photo of the *Spray* which had been given to her family by Victor Slocum when he visited Sydney at one time. Her father had presented it to the St. George Motor Boat Club, of which he was a member. I visited the club and saw the photo, an enlarged copy of the well-known one taken of the *Spray* sailing in Sydney Harbor.

I also discovered some entirely new photographs of the *Spray*. K. B. Johnstone, owner of the St. Kilda *Spray*, wrote:

"I have a photo of her sailing up Port Jackson with Slocum at the helm." Some time later, he sent it to me—a different one from the other harbor photo already referred to.

In his book, Slocum wrote: "Summer was approaching, and the harbor of Sydney was blooming with yachts. Some of them came down to the weather-beaten *Spray* and sailed round her at Shelcote, where she took a berth for a few days." [4] Shelcote is now called Shell Cove and was named after a large house standing in five acres of land, the residence of the late Alexander Oliver, M.A. His son, Francis B. Oliver, sent me a photograph of the *Spray* anchored here. The large house, Shelcote, shown in the background is still standing although badly damaged by fire some years ago. The boat shed visible behind the *Spray*'s bowsprit is now in ruins, although the piles in front of it still remain. They are of turpentine, an Australian hardwood which has been proven the best timber in the world for durability in the water and resistance to marine borers. Although it is over sixty years since the photograph was taken, those original piles are still in good condition. This photograph of the *Spray* was taken by the late Staunton W. Spain, and his son Captain Stanley Spain, a well-known Sydney yachtsman, was aboard the *Spray* several times during her stay in Shell Cove. In a letter, he said that Alexander Oliver had a suit of sails made for the *Spray* and gave it to Slocum. Strangely enough, Slocum makes no mention of this in his book, although he refers to a new suit of sails given him by Commodore Mark Foy. [5]

A few days after this photograph was received, another Sydney man sent along a larger but identical print, and some months later a gentleman in Tasmania told me that he had one also. Apparently this picture of the *Spray* was widely circulated at the time.

While browsing through the April 1959 issue of *Maine Coast Fisherman*, I came across a letter to the editor by William A. Nickerson of Massachusetts, and a photo of the *Spray*. To quote from the letter:

I am taking the liberty of writing to you at this time because of my interest in your article printed in the February issue of your Maine Coast Fisherman, telling the story of Capt. Joshua Slocum. I think that I was one of the first people on Cape Cod to get and read his "Sailing Alone Around the World." And to say I enjoyed it would be putting it mildly. . . .

I'm enclosing a rather poor snapshot of the *Spray* as she lay at anchor in the harbour at Cotuit, Cape Cod, Mass., in the summer of 1908. It was taken by one of three young men, of whom I was one, from a cat-boat in which the three were just starting off on a two-week cruise—Buzzard's Bay, Narragansett Bay, and Vineyard Sound ports.

About ten days later, on our return trip, we sailed into Oak Bluffs, Martha's Vineyard, and, to our surprise, found the *Spray* at anchor there. The next three days were a sort of nightmare— a real old-fashioned No'easter. Our boat dragged anchor, but we were able to get a line to the stern of a motor boat moored to a state mooring and held on. The *Spray* wasn't so fortunate. She dragged ashore—on a sand beach, however, so wasn't damaged.

After the storm was over, we sailed for home. The *Spray* was still there when we left.

I wrote Mr. Nickerson and he sent me a copy of the photograph. He said that after carefully thinking over the affair, he had decided it was the summer of 1909, not 1908, as stated, for in the latter year he had been away with his mother in Nova Scotia. He also said that later in that same year he had seen the *Spray*, he heard a rumor that she had sailed south on an exploration trip to the Orinoco River. This seems to confirm the date as 1909, and that photograph is the last one ever taken of the *Spray* which has so far been published.

Finally, a note to correct a mistake. The picture in Peter Freuchen's *Book of the Seven Seas* labeled "Joshua Slocum's *Spray*" is not the original *Spray* at all, but the copy built at Oxford, Maryland, by Captain R. D. Culler.

10

CHANGES IN THE RIG

One of the most interesting facts about the *Spray* brought to light by photographs is that major modifications were made to her sail plan after her world voyage. The change from sloop to yawl in South American waters is, of course, well known, but later alterations are apparent from photographs taken late in her career, and only recently discovered. A careful chronological study of all *Spray* photographs available reveals an interesting progression.

When Slocum found the old *Spray*, her hull was unusual for a yacht, but there was nothing extreme about her sail plan. He rigged her like a typical coaster of the period; her gear had been worked out on hundreds of similar vessels. The *Spray* had a long bowsprit and boom, a stumpy mast, and a big mainsail by present day standards. A wooden outrigger set a couple of feet over the stern was no doubt useful when reefing. In his father's biography Victor Slocum wrote: "When first rigged, the *Spray* was a double-head rigged sloop. . . ." [1] This might seem rather a contradiction to modern yachtsmen, accustomed to regarding any boat with two headsails as a cutter, but it was not uncommon for old time American sloops to carry two sails ahead of the mast. Because of the forward position of the mast, however, they still remained sloops technically. The *Spray*'s original rig is clearly shown in the drawing of her at anchor off Gibraltar by George Varian. It was probably taken from a photograph, like many of this artist's other drawings of the boat.

Slocum also carried a big jib, the so-called "jumbo" which was very popular on the fishing sloops and schooners of his day. This filled almost the whole fore triangle, like a modern Genoa, and it seems that Slocum used it as a working sail in preference to the two separate headsails, particularly later on in his world trip. Almost all photos of the *Spray* show only this one big jib, with the staysail stay removed. This would have interfered with the jib when tacking. No doubt the single big sail proved more efficient than two smaller ones, and, with only one pair of sheets to worry about instead of two, easier to handle. In heavy winds, Slocum had the choice of reefing it, or dropping it altogether and setting up the storm jib and/or staysail on its stay, which could quickly be set up again. It is apparent from photographs of the *Spray* that Slocum did, in fact, carry his big jib only, or jib and staysail on their stays, according to conditions. The Gibraltar drawing shows two headsails, as does the photograph of the *Spray* in Shell Cove. In the one taken a few days later, as she left Sydney, the staysail stay is removed and only the big jib set. A picture of her ashore at the Cocos Islands shows the inner stay set up again and two headsails furled. In photographs of the *Spray* taken after her circumnavigation, only the big jib is visible and this is shown in the yawl sail plan in Slocum's book.

The *Spray* originally carried a topmast. Victor Slocum wrote that the mast ". . . was fitted with a square doubling with cross-tree cap and topmast." [2] Doubtless a topsail would have proved useful in the light winds common along the New England coast where Slocum spent a season getting to know his craft. Out at sea, however, it would have been a handful for one man to look after, and at Yarmouth, his last American port, Slocum dispensed with it. He wrote: "I now stowed all my goods securely, for the boisterous Atlantic was before me, and I sent the topmast down, knowing that the *Spray* would be the wholesomer with it on deck." [3] This is the only time Slocum mentions the topmast, and no photographs of the *Spray* before she set out on her world trip (which would have shown it), have so far been discovered. The earliest picture of the *Spray* is the drawing of her at Gibraltar, and the topmast cap at the truck is clearly visible. A photograph taken in a South American port just before her mast was shortened unfortunately shows only the lower part. On the title page of Victor's biography there is a silhouette of the *Spray* with all canvas set, including topsail, drawn by the artist J. Warren Sheppard.

The only other light-weather sail which the *Spray* carried was a flying jib, made by a woman on Juan Fernandez. Slocum first mentioned using it on the trade wind run across the Indian Ocean. In the Arafura Sea, the *Spray* encountered light winds, and Slocum wrote, "I got out the flying-jib made at Juan Fernandez, and set it as a spinnaker from the stoutest bamboo that Mrs. Stevenson had given me at Samoa. The spinnaker pulled like a sodger, and the bamboo holding its own, the *Spray* mended her pace." [4] He also used it on the passage from Cape Town to St. Helena, and it proved its worth in fresh winds as well as light. In the sail plan of the *Spray*, the bamboo pole is shown lashed to the bowsprit, and no doubt the sail would have been more controllable this way than set as a spinnaker. All photographs taken after 1905 show this pole, so Slocum must have decided to make it a permanent fitting. It would have been a useful sail with the light winds predominating in the coastal cruising he did then and later in the West Indies.

It was in South America that the first major change was made in the *Spray*'s rig. When the vessel was struck by a big wave during the desperate race with the Moorish pirate vessel after leaving Gibraltar, the mainsheet strop parted and the boom was hurled against the shrouds, breaking just behind the jaws. Slocum lashed it up temporarily and at his next port of call,

80

Pernambuco in Brazil, set to work to repair it. It was simple enough to remove the short broken part and refit the jaws. This shortened the boom by about four feet. A couple of the after cloths in the mainsail must have been removed at the same time and the leech reroped, to fit the boom, but Slocum makes no mention of this. He sailed on to Rio de Janeiro, as he said: "without any event worth mentioning. . . ." Slocum was never one to go much into details in his book, particularly with the more technical aspects of the *Spray*, and in so few words, dismisses what may have been a significant stage in the voyage. It is very likely that this twelve-day passage with a shorter boom and smaller sail, making one hundred miles a day along the coast, brought home to him the advantages of a reduced rig, and reflection on the heavier weather farther south would make it seem more attractive still. Whether or not the boom accident did, in fact, underlie Slocum's decision to modify the rig of the *Spray* must remain a subject of conjecture, but at Rio the change began in earnest. He wrote: "As I had decided to give the *Spray* a yawl rig for the tempestuous waters of Patagonia, I here placed on the stern a semicircular brace to support a jigger mast." [5] Farther down the coast more alterations were made. "I unshipped the sloop's mast at Buenos Aires and shortened it by seven feet. I reduced the length of the bowsprit by about five feet, and even then I found it reaching far enough from home; and more than once, when on the end of it reefing the jib, I regretted that I had not shortened it another foot." [6] Although the yawl rig was intended specifically for the rough weather of Patagonia, strangely enough Slocum left it until this was behind him before fitting the second mast. It was at Port Angosto, his last anchorage in the Strait, that he finally shipped the jigger, "which changed the rig to a yawl, though I called the boat a sloop just the same, the jigger being merely a temporary affair." [7] Probably he found the smaller mainsail sufficient improvement in itself as to make the addition of a mizzen seem not as necessary as he might at first have thought. Another four feet had to be cut off the boom, the outboard end this time, to enable it to clear the jigger.

Slocum enlarged on the rig modifications in a letter to his publishers:

I should have mentioned that the jigger-mast which I shipped at Port Angosto was taken on board while at St. Mary's Bay where I found it among drift-wood on the beach. It was one of those "hardy spruce" saplings.

The boom . . . was previously broken in the gale off the coast of Morocco and was fished then, near the mainmast. The short broken end was removed at Pernambuco and the jaws refitted— this brought the boom in about four feet but left some four feet still projecting over the stern until she was refitted as before stated, at Port Angosto.[8]

Slocum also fitted a V-shaped bumkin, projecting about eight feet over the stern, to take the mizzen sheet.

The sail itself was rather an unusual affair—a combination of spritsail and standing lug. The foot was not laced to a spar, but set on a sprit-boom, with its fore end carried in a rope snotter several feet above the tack. Such sprit-booms were not uncommonly used in American small sailing craft of the last century, but usually with jib-headed sails. With a gaff it was employed rarely, if at all, and Slocum's use of it with a lug-type yard may be unique.

The next changes in the *Spray*'s rig were not made until several years after her return to America. Most of this time the Captain spent in some quiet local sailing on the New England coast, but then he felt the urge to go farther afield once again. In 1905 he sailed south on a winter cruise to the West Indies, singlehanded as usual, and he did this round trip in 1906, 1907, and 1908. No doubt his visits to the islands were responsible for further modifications to the *Spray*'s rig, which began in 1906, after his first cruise. A photograph of the *Spray* at Jamaica in February 1906 shows no change, while in one taken at Oyster Bay, Long Island, after her return north, there is a modified mizzen bumkin. The original outrigger crosspiece has been removed and the V-shaped bumkin, which had been fitted in South America, replaced by a single pole set lower down on the stern. The same arrangement is also visible in photos taken at Washington, D. C., in May 1907. A picture of the *Spray* at Miami, Florida, in January 1908, when Slocum was heading south on a visit to the Bahamas, shows the mainsail jib-headed. The new sail would have been the so-called "leg-o'-mutton" sail, widely used in the days before the true Bermudian mainsail, with its long luff, became popular. It was a triangular sail with the luff not much longer than the foot. Although not as close-winded as its modern counterpart, it had the advantage of being able to be set on a much shorter mast, and Slocum could have used it with no modification to his existing rigging. It seems that this sail was employed as an alternative to his gaff mainsail rather than a replacement, for a photo captioned "Returned from the West Indies in 1908," published in the editorial section of *Yachting Monthly* for April 1918, shows the *Spray* with her old gaff sail. The picture was taken in the early summer of 1908.

A photograph of the *Spray* under sail in Branford Harbor, Connecticut, shows further modification to the rig. The date is uncertain, but in view of the changes to her rig and the boat's movements around this time, it must have been 1908 or 1909. The *Spray* is seen on a close reach in a light breeze, and the very slight wake shows that she is only just moving. With the anchor hanging low down from the bow, it looks as if Slocum is coming up to an anchorage, or has just got under way from it. The rig shows marked evidence of the *Spray*'s visit to the Bahamas, and in place of the old gaff or the jib-headed mainsail of earlier photos, the vessel is sporting a leg-o'-mutton sail very similar to those commonly used in the Islands. Instead of the large headboard typically employed in the Bahama sails, however, there is a short curved bamboo club at the peak. Archibald B. Roosevelt recalled that the *Spray* was using this sail when he sailed on her in August 1906: " . . . she had a jib-headed or leg-o'-mutton mainsail (I never remember him using the jigger). As I recollect it the jib-head was sort of a square jib-head with a little bit of a sprit maybe a foot or two long and hoisted by what ordinarily would have been the throat halyard. I believe I recollect his saying to me that it was

83

much easier to handle than the gaff-headed rig. . . . Captain
Slocum told us that he broke the gaff and replaced it with the
leg-o'-mutton mainsail."

The mizzen in the photograph is a true jib-headed leg-o'-
mutton sail with its luff set on mast hoops and its foot laced to
a boom pivoted low down on the mast. Both the luff and foot
are longer than in the original lugsail Slocum carried, and the
new mizzen would probably have been a more efficient sail
on the wind. To use this jib-headed sail of longer luff on the
same mast was doubtless why Slocum fitted a new bumkin
after his first West Indies cruise. Very likely this sail was given
to him; most of the changes to the *Spray*'s rig seemed to come
about as a result of accidents or coincidence. Apparently she
was sailing with her leg-o'-mutton mizzen from 1906 on, but
photographs taken at this time show the sail furled up with
its boom to the mast, and looking no different from the original lug.

Other new features in the Branford Harbor view are a boom
laced to the foot of the jib, wooden ratlines in the starboard
shrouds and a light "topmast," apparently for the burgee; it
seems too frail to support any topsail. Slocum was certainly
taking more of an interest in the rig of his boat, and showing
that he was not yet too old to learn new ways. The changes
were undoubtedly an improvement on the *Spray*'s original
rig for the coastal sailing she was then doing.

Although the change to a jib-headed mizzen appears to have
been a permanent one, Slocum did not discard his gaff sail
altogether in favor of the new leg-o'-mutton rig. Like his other
jib-headed main, this sail apparently served as an alternative.
This is borne out by the photographs, in which the hoops for
the gaff sail are still carried on the mast, resting on the boom
jaws, while the new mainsail is set on a jackstay. With this
arrangement, either sail could be used without interfering
with the other and with no modification to the mast or rigging.

The most recent photograph of the *Spray* so far published
was taken in the summer of 1909 at Cotuit Harbor, Massachusetts. The *Spray* is at anchor with sails furled, and the
rounded head of the leg-o'-mutton mainsail can be made out

84

near the boom jaws. The unattached hoops on the mast indicate that Slocum had not given up the idea of using his gaff sail entirely. Some months after this picture was taken, the *Spray* set out on her customary winter cruise down south. She was never seen again. One wonders which rig Slocum chose for this—his last voyage.

THE LAST VOYAGE

As the years passed, Slocum's plans became more ambitious. Each winter after 1905 he had spent in the West Indies, but apparently he wanted to go farther afield. The Captain, now sixty five years old, was planning a sensational exploration trip to South America. Thomas Fleming Day, *Rudder*'s editor, wrote: ". . . he told me that he was going up the Orinoco River, and through the Rio Negro into the Amazon and home that way, and that he expected to be away for about two years." [1]

To get ready for the venture, Slocum took the *Spray* to the famous Herreshoff works in Bristol, Rhode Island. Victor wrote that she was "fitted out" there, and continued: "Mr. Herreshoff (the great 'Nat') admired his visitor and said she was a good boat. While the *Spray* was in his yard he spent considerable time looking her over and also much time in conversation with her skipper, though Nat was known to be a man who wasted neither time nor words. When the *Spray* left Bristol in the autumn of 1909, she was well fitted and provided for.

. . ." [2] One would infer from the above that the Herreshoff yard did the fitting out on the *Spray*, but this was not so. L. Francis Herreshoff, who saw the vessel at this time, said: "The *Spray* did not have any work done on her at the Herreshoff Company but simply lay at one of their wharves in what is called Walker's Cove. She may have been given some old ropes, but the captain did everything himself in the refit." [3]

On November 14, 1909, Slocum set sail again, alone. Nothing further was ever heard of the old captain or his *Spray;* both vanished into history.

Many theories have been advanced to account for the loss of the *Spray*, but none has been proved, since no trace of the vessel has ever been found. A number of people, who saw the *Spray* in her last years, thought that she was poorly constructed and finally "fell apart" in mid-ocean. Recalling his visit to the boat in 1908, Harold S. Smith wrote: "She was also a remarkable example of exceedingly poor construction and I was not the least surprised when she went missing the year after I boarded her."

Charles D. Mower, who measured the *Spray* on her return from the world trip, reported that while her hull and deck were very sturdy, the deckhouses were light and flimsy. He attributed her loss to these finally giving way. [4]

H. S. ("Skipper") Smith was another who saw the *Spray* late in her career. He commented on her loss in *Rudder* magazine:

The old boat was in pretty bad shape when I last saw her in 1908. Her rebuilding in 1892–94 had been a haphazard sort of a job and any and all materials were used in the process. In fact no two planks seemed to be of the same kind of wood. To tell the truth, Captain Slocum was very much what I term a "hammer and nails" carpenter. In other words, if a three-inch nail could not be trusted to send a plank home when hit with the hammer, the Old Man would be apt to try a six-inch spike and a maul, and if it split a timber in the process it was just too bad. Slocum never seemed to worry very much about anything he could not see. In consequence, the rebuilt *Spray*'s life was short, and I have no doubt that when the captain put out to sea on what proved to be her final voyage she slowly disintegrated.[5]

Thomas Fleming Day held a similar view, and, in an editorial in *Rudder*, wrote, "I expect the old sloop spewed a plank; she was getting considerably dozy the last time I looked her over. Even in the early days of her rejuvenation she was not of the strongest, being built of whatever came to hand and cost least. . . ." [6]

These comments appear to conflict with many of Slocum's own statements about the strength of the *Spray*'s construction. We read that the scantlings of the various members were far in excess of those usually employed on a boat of her size, and that certain fittings were added with strength alone in mind. The after cabin had a stanchion in the middle to prevent the top being smashed down by heavy seas; there were no port lights at all with their attendant weaknesses; a double set of breasthooks was fitted, so that she might "shunt ice" if need be; the planking was carefully done, and Slocum wrote of the seams: "the inner edges were so close that I could not see daylight between them." All the butts were fastened by through bolts, and ". . . Many bolts with screw-nuts were used in other parts of the construction, in all about a thousand. It was my purpose to make my vessel stout and strong." [7]

Even allowing for some understandable exaggeration on Slocum's part, the facts of the world voyage itself seem to confirm the *Spray*'s sturdiness, at least as far as her hull was concerned.

On the passage to Nova Scotia from Gloucester, Slocum was wrongly directed by a fisherman, and "the *Spray* sailed directly over the southwest ledge through the worst tiderace in the Bay of Fundy. . . ." [8] He wrote of the "terrible thrashing I got in the fierce sou'west rip . . ." but added, "I overhauled the *Spray* once more and tried her seams, but found that even the test of the sou'west rip had started nothing." [9]

The *Spray* met her most severe trial in the terrific gale off Cape Horn. "It was indeed a mountainous sea. When the sloop was in the fiercest squalls, with only the reefed forestaysail set, even that small sail shook her from keelson to truck when it shivered by the leech. Had I harbored the shadow of a doubt for her safety, it would have been that she might spring a leak in the garboard at the heel of the mast; but she never called me once to the pump." [10]

Later, in Tasmania, "The *Spray* was hauled out on the marine railway at Devonport and examined carefully top and bottom, but was found absolutely free from the destructive teredo, and sound in all respects." [11]

A few days from the end of the voyage, the little vessel was badly shaken up again, this time in cross seas whipped up by a gale in the turbulent Gulf Stream. Under the strain, the jib-stay broke and the mast, deprived of all support forward, twitched about like a reed. Slocum managed to climb up and repair it temporarily. "Had the *Spray*'s mast not been well stepped, however, it would have been 'John Walker' when the stay broke. Good work in the building of my vessel stood me always in good stead." [12]

After the completion of his round-the-world trip, Slocum wrote: "My ship was also in better condition than when she sailed from Boston on her long voyage. She was still as sound as a nut, and as tight as the best ship afloat. She did not leak a drop—not one drop! The pump, which had been little used before reaching Australia, had not been rigged since that at all." [13]

In the summer of 1908, a year before he disappeared, Slocum spoke of his boat to reporters: "I caulked her myself, fourteen years ago, and she has scraped mud and sand off the land of a hundred coasts. I never knew her to leak, and the caulking is as tight and as secure as the day I put it in. Some friends told me it would crawl, but it hasn't yet." [14] Surely no sign, this, of a boat "disintegrating" from old age!

Certainly, right through her career, the *Spray* never gave any signs of falling apart from poor construction—rather the opposite. The fact that the *Spray* was built "on the cheap"— from timbers which happened to be on hand at the time—has little bearing on her strength or longevity. Many vessels were, in the past, put together in just such a way, even from drift-wood, simply because of economic necessity, and some can still be seen today, in many parts of the world, as active as ever, after long careers as working boats. There are more important factors determining the life of a boat than the sort of wood it is built of—or its cost. If the *Spray*'s loss was due to some weakness in the vessel herself, one must look further than the hull. L. Francis Herreshoff reported that when he saw her, some of her gear was very light and weak.[15] In photographs of the vessel at this time, however, both her standing rigging and running gear generally seem quite adequate. In some photos, the mainsheet, an inverted luff tackle, looks very light—hardly more than one inch in circumference. In comparison, the foot lacing of the mainsail around the boom—a relatively much less important item—appears about twice this size! I imagine Slocum made do with whatever was available at the time, without being too concerned about what might have been better. He was nothing if not an opportunist.

But whatever the strength of the *Spray* and her gear, there is no doubt at all that Slocum became very careless about maintenance. This was apparent to many people who visited the vessel after her world voyage. The late Ernest J. Dean of Chilmark was a young yachtsman who saw much of the *Spray*. He said: "The captain grew slack in keeping her up. When I first met him and the *Spray*, they both were neat, trim and sea-worthy, but as the years rolled along, I noticed signs of wear and exposure." [16] Captain Donald Poole, also of Chilmark, said of the *Spray* that "her rigging was slack and in need of tarring, and Irish pennants were much in evidence." [17] Percy E. Bud-long, who was aboard the *Spray* on two occasions at Washington in May 1907, wrote: "To be sure, she was rather shabby as to paint. . . ." [18]

In photographs of the *Spray* at this time, there are obvious signs of neglect about the decks and hull. However, just how much of this deterioration was superficial and how much was deep-seated, it is hard to tell. A boat can look very shabby and completely run down, and yet, beneath, be perfectly sound and seaworthy. The *Spray*'s strength, as best shown by her continued tightness, would have left plenty of reserve for abuse

90

and neglect, far more, in fact, than she may have got in the ten years or so before she disappeared. In her vanishing suddenly without any trace at all, I feel one must look for much more severe causes than the likelihood of dry rot, broken sheets, weak sails, or even parted shrouds, such as might result from neglect over the years.

Victor Slocum, who probably knew the *Spray* better than anyone except his father, believed that she was cut down at night by a steamer. This is by far the most logical explanation so far put forward to account for her complete disappearance. Victor wrote:

The events at sea following his departure are matters of conjecture. Anyone's guess is as good as another's. Four things may have happened to the vessel and her skipper: Foundering in a gale, which is unlikely, as there was no seriously bad weather which that pair could not ride out to the sea anchor which was always ready; second, the possibility of fire, a hazard imminent on every vessel everywhere; third, collision at night; and last, shipwreck.

Collision at night has always seemed to me the most likely of any of the things that may have happened, for after the introduction of steamboating, all sailing vessels, great and small, had constantly to be on the alert against collision with a steamer at night, especially in coastal waters. A sailing vessel's running lights, sometimes partly screened by the vessel's own sails, were never entirely depended upon for protection. A flare torch was always kept ready for instant ignition. This was displayed in such a manner as to light up the sails and thus warn off a steamer coming on. The *Spray*, like any other sailing vessel, carried a turpentine-filled flare within quick reach in the after companionway. After clearing Hatteras she would have been reasonably safe from collision for the rest of the passage, but up to that point there were three different great steamship tracks to cross: those out of New York, Philadelphia, and the ports of Chesapeake Bay; all very dangerous at night for small sailing vessels with dim oil-burning sidelights. Even a steamer with good look-outs on the forecastle and intense vigilance on the bridge, travelling at eighteen knots, could run down such a small vessel without ever seeing it or feeling the impact.[19]

91

One interesting thing in this regard is that the *Spray* apparently never carried any navigation lights. No photographs of the vessel show any of the usual wooden screens for port and starboard lights in the rigging, and Slocum himself never mentioned using them. Victor must have been aware of this, and it is odd that he did not refer to it in the above context. Sailing vessels of less than 20 tons gross are not obliged under international regulations to carry their running lights in position, and many small yachts like the *Spray* carry none, relying instead on lanterns or torches. Slocum used to hang a powerful fisherman's lamp in the rigging, which he said threw a light a great distance around. He added: "Indeed a ship that would run another down having such a good light aboard would be capable of running into a light-ship." [20]

However careless Slocum may have become in keeping the *Spray* shipshape after his world trip, there is no doubt that before and during it, he was careful and vigilant in all matters pertaining to seaworthiness. At the start of the Atlantic crossing, he took stock of the rigging and gear, stowing everything securely and taking the topmast down. "I gave the lanyards a pull and hitched them afresh, and saw that the gammon was secure, also that the boat was lashed, for even in summer one may meet with bad weather in the crossing." [21]

In other matters, too, he was equally careful. While cutting firewood in the Magellan Strait, he had to be on the alert against savage Indians. "I have described my method of wooding up in detail, that the reader who has kindly borne with me so far may see that in this, as in all other particulars of my voyage, I took great care against all kinds of surprises, whether by animals or by the elements. In the Strait of Magellan the greatest vigilance was necessary. In this instance I reasoned that I had all about me the greatest danger of the whole voyage— the treachery of cunning savages, for which I must be particularly on the alert." [22]

Despite even the best vigilance, however, accidents still happen. Slocum wrote of one near miss while sailing in the southeast trades from Marquesas to Samoa. This was a ". . . narrow escape from collision with a great whale that was absent-mindedly ploughing the ocean at night while I was below. The noise from his startled snort and the commotion he made in the sea, as he turned to clear my vessel, brought me on deck in time to catch a wetting from the water he threw up with his flukes. The monster was apparently frightened. He headed quickly for the east; I kept on going west." [23]

The alertness Slocum displayed against the Patagonian savages would have been of little value to him in combating their more sophisticated brethren farther north cutting through the night at twenty knots. Perhaps there was one ocean liner not quite so obliging as that whale.

Slocum's practice of letting the *Spray* sail herself through the night may have been all right in the lonely sea wastes, far away from the tracks of steamers, but it was hardly suitable for the east coast of the United States. For a single-hander to let his boat sail unwatched under such conditions is nothing short of sheer folly; it could be excused only on the grounds of utter exhaustion, and this was not so in the *Spray*'s case, for Slocum had just started out on his voyage.

One copy of the *Spray*, the *Pandora*, was lost in approximately the same region off Cape Hatteras where the original *Spray* is presumed to have disappeared. It is likely that she, too, was cut down at night. A letter by "Memory" in an old *Yachting Monthly* referred to this vessel:

I remember reading in the "Rudder" of a boat called *Pandora*, built in Australia on the lines of *Spray*, and navigated by two sporting sailor men crossing the Pacific, and after capsizing off the Horn arrived safely in New York, where in an interview with that intrepid sailor man T. F. Day they spoke of their possessing this self-steering quality in a marked degree, which obviously must make for the most delightful voyaging. If I remember right, he replied warning them of the danger in sailing at night with the wheel lashed and no one on deck, acquiring by so doing a false sense of security. . . . *Pandora* left New York bound for Europe, and was never heard of again. A subsequent letter in the "Yachtsman" conjectured that she had been run into and sunk by a German liner whilst hove to at night.[24]

Whatever the fate of the *Spray*, it must ever be a mystery. A strange coincidence, this; the *Spray* remains as much of an enigma in her passing as in her origin.

PROS AND CONS

The *Spray* has always been a controversial vessel. Even when Slocum found her she was long out of date, and, compared with the average modern yacht, she is of course quite antique. The arguments about her have been loud and long, and she is still a sure conversation piece in any yachting group. Whatever is said about the old boat, the fact remains that she and her skipper established for themselves an unparalleled place in yachting history, and will ever be remembered with affection by those who "go down to the sea in ships."

In my extensive search for information on the *Spray*, I suppose I have come across most of the different ideas which people hold about her. Some are true, some are false, but, all together, they form an interesting rider to the *Spray* story itself.

In his story of the circumnavigation, Slocum did not treat the *Spray*'s behavior at great length, but he did set out clearly enough what she *did* do. In the face of this, it is really astonishing how many erroneous ideas about her have grown up, even

94

among those who claim to have read the book. There are those who say that Slocum spun a good yarn, but not a true one —that most of the glowing claims for the *Spray* were due to Slocum's exaggeration or to the literary efforts of his editor. It is, of course, their own business whether or not they believe it; the evidence of port records, newspaper accounts and the like, is sufficient verification of his passages, even without the evidence of those who sailed on the *Spray* and the many who have built and sailed copies of her since.

The very disappearance of the *Spray* is taken by some as sure proof of her poor qualities. One person wrote to me: "The important thing is that in the end *Spray* disappeared and Slocum with her." Such a viewpoint is as novel as it is ridiculous, but is rather an unkind cut at the old boat which did so much. No one knows the facts of the *Spray*'s passing, but whatever happened to her is in no way a reflection on her seaworthiness, proven beyond doubt on her world voyage. To spring a serious leak, to collide with a steamer—these have happened to thousands of vessels, and as for foundering in a gale—there are storms that can overwhelm any ship, regardless of model.

A lot of people, while admitting that the *Spray* had some good points, maintain that it was the man who counted—not the boat. Slocum, they say, was successful, not because of the *Spray*, but in spite of her! That may be true; Slocum could probably have gone around the world in a hollow log— Voss did—but it is not the whole truth, as even a passing glance at the facts of the *Spray*'s ocean crossings will show. The boat *did* count, and very much. Certainly Joshua Slocum was a great seaman and an amazing navigator; no one will ever doubt that, or the part that luck played in his voyage. However, luck counts as much as experience in any venture, and Slocum's circumnavigation shows clearly that these qualities alone were not responsible for the success of his voyage.

Of experience, the captain wrote: "I was born in the breezes, and I had studied the sea as perhaps few men have studied it, neglecting all else. . . . Thus the voyage which I am now to narrate was a natural outcome not only of my love of adventure, but of my lifelong experience." [1] He well knew, too,

that other things are just as important as experience: "to in-
sure a reasonable measure of success, experience should sail
with the ship. But in order to be a successful navigator or
sailor it is not necessary to hang a tar-bucket about one's
neck. . . . I myself learned more seamanship, I think, on the
Spray than on any other ship I ever sailed. . . ." [2]

Slocum, in fact, nearly wrecked the *Spray* before the world
trip had even begun. His son Garfield told about it in a letter
to Walter Magnes Teller. He said that he was with his father
"on board the *Spray*, outbound from an inlet on the Maine
coast. There was very little wind. Father was steering. As the
Spray almost passed a ledge on the leeward, the powerful
undertow lifted her and dropped her on the ledge. The waves
tried to finish the *Spray*. Some help came quickly to our aid
by land and sea. Father threw a coil of rope to some men on
shore. He tied me under my arm pits, held one end of the
rope, and told me to jump. The men pulled me to high ground.
Other men, in dories, got the *Spray* off, and towed her to a
place where father repaired her bottom." [3]

Some people have said that the *Spray* could just as well
have been any other decrepit hulk which came into Slocum's
possession by chance. Granted, and it might also have taken
him around the world—after a fashion. However, the fact is
that fate provided him with an eminently suitable vessel—
Slocum himself admitted that—and the similar qualities of many
copies built since and sailed extensively by men far less skilled
than he, have shown that it was not only the man who counted.
Roger Strout, for instance, who took his copy, the *Igdrasil*,
around the world, learned to sail on the initial leg of the
cruise. The *Igdrasil* was his first boat; before that, he had
never owned anything larger than a canoe!

No, one cannot deny that the *Spray* played her part in the
success of the voyage. In the words of the captain's eldest
son Victor: "Indeed, the key to the first singlehanded voyage
around the world can be found in the right little ship and
the right man to sail her." [4]

The *Spray* is criticized more on the grounds of her ancient
lineage than anything else. The editor of one magazine summed

up the general attitude in his reply to a letter of mine: "The *Spray* was by no means an ideal vessel and a yacht of modern design is incomparably better in all respects."

Doubtless the *Spray* has definite disadvantages compared to the modern yacht. Her relative slowness in tacking and her heavier gear are sure drawbacks for harbor and coastal sailing, while her design is inferior for racing. In short, for those conditions with which the present-day yachtsman is most concerned, the *Spray* is right out of her element, and this makes her objectionable to many. However, it should be borne in mind that this is not the type of environment for which she was intended. There is no such thing as the "ideal" boat; all boats have their limitations, the modern yacht included, and have to be sailed with these in view. Antiquity alone is no valid condemnation of any vessel. The *Spray* type has gone, and her form is strikingly different from that most sought after in her own day, but does that make it any the less worthwhile? The model of boats has changed, but so has the type of sailing. Regardless of rating rules and social standards, the oceans are still the same as they were, and the design of the older vessels can prove just as effective as ever. The draft horse cannot beat the race horse at his own game—but remember that it works both ways.

13

COPIES OF THE "SPRAY"

It is now over sixty years since Captain Joshua Slocum completed his voyage around the world, making for himself and his *Spray* a place in history with what is regarded as the greatest yachting achievement of all time. Inspired by Slocum's narrative, and the faith he had in the qualities of the *Spray*, many others have built ships on her lines. I doubt if there has been any other boat which has so aroused the interest and imagination of boat lovers the world over and tempted men to build copies. Some have kept faithfully to the published lines, others have modified them in all kinds of ways; even enlarged and reduced versions have been built. The rigs used have been as varied as the hulls, covering almost the entire range of fore and aft types. In all, they make a very interesting collection. Let us now find out something about these vessels —when they were built, where, and what their owners' reasons were.

THE ROCHESTER *Spray*

Since Joshua Slocum is remembered as America's outstanding sailor, and his *Spray* was a typically American vessel, one might have expected the first boat on her lines to have been built in America. In fact, this was not so, although more *Spray* copies have originated from this country than from any other. The first replica was built at Rochester, England, in 1902. It was also one of the largest—54 feet overall. A letter by Frank Gilliland in a 1918 issue of *Yachting Monthly* said: "I always thought a *Spray* had been built some 10–15 years ago either in the Medway or Burnham districts, identical as far as hull was concerned, with Captain Slocum's vessel." [1] In the next issue, a letter by "XXXVII 190" confirmed this: "Your correspondent is correct as to a copy of *Spray* having been built by Gill of Rochester. Shortly afterwards she was advertised for sale in the 'Yachtsman,' where an illustration showed her to have been given a more modern and yachty appearance above water than the original." [2] Apparently the editor of *Yachting Monthly* ten years later was unaware of this correspondence. A letter by Norman Deakin in a 1928 issue stated:

On page 61 of [the November] Yachting Monthly, with reference to shallow-draught cruisers, I see you state that as far as you can ascertain no boat on the lines of *Spray* has been built in England.

This is not so as a *Spray* was built to somewhere near the lines by Gill, of Rochester, in 1902, and had a counter added by Stow in the following year. I remember seeing her underway many times. She was of varnished teak. She was sold abroad to Hamburg. You can see her dimensions in any Lloyds prior to 1914 (L.B.P. 42.6 ft., L.W.L. 441 ft. (sic), beam 14.1 ft., depth 5.65 ft. Kelvin 4-cyl. 1912).

The son of the builder, Maurice O. Gill, of Rochester, wrote me as follows: "Your letter of the 28th July addressed to the Mayor of Rochester, ultimately found its way to me, as being one of the few remaining members of the Gill family to whom you have referred.

"My father, E. A. Gill, referred to in the attached letter, died

99

A. Sail Plan of the *Spray*

Drawn and modified by Kenneth E. Slack, March 1962

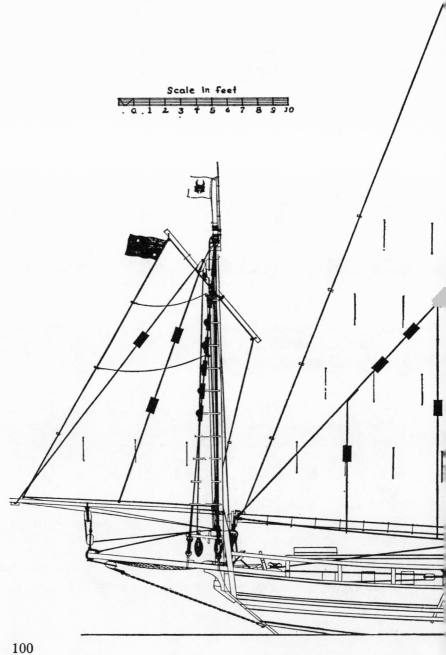

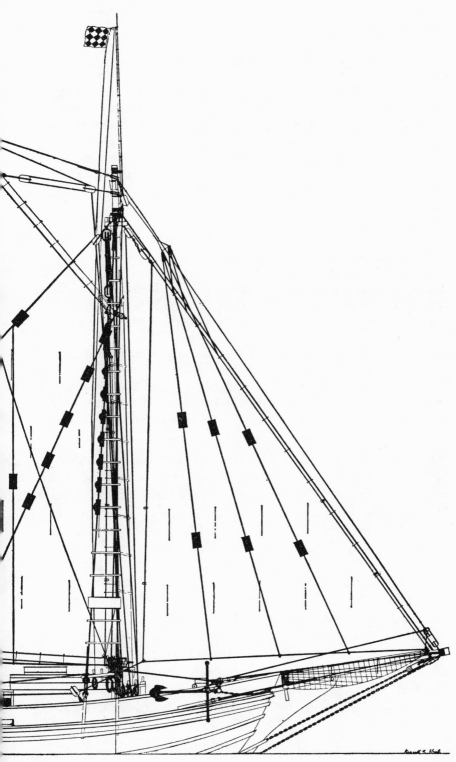

in 1953 at the age of 88 and was probably the last living person able to answer your questions.

"The firm of Gill & Sons existed until the early part of this century and was finally run by my father's eldest brother, George, who has possibly been dead for 30 years, and I am afraid that there are no records of the firm available to me.

"In an endeavour to help, however, I, as a member of the Committee of Lloyd's Register of Shipping, asked the Yacht Department whether they could help me, and I am enclosing a copy of a letter I have received from them." [3]

The letter said:

The yacht was a wood cutter, length b.p. 42 ft. and W.L. 40 ft., breadth 14 ft., depth 6 ft. and built by your ancestor at Rochester in 1902 for a Mr. A. E. Mason. The design is credited to E. A. Gill, but was presumably taken from the published lines of the noted *Spray*, in which Captain Joshua Slocum circumnavigated the world in the 1890s.

In 1912 she became the property of Gustav Kruger of Hamburg and was converted to an auxiliary yawl in 1914. She next appears in the Yacht Register in 1926 under the name of *Drei Rosen* and her owner was Fritz Leisegang of Stettin. From that date onwards I can only presume that her owner declined to send in the requisite annual particulars.

In a 1929 issue of *Yachting Monthly*, a letter by Otto A. Erdmann of Berlin gave some further information on the vessel: "I have read with interest the comment Mr. Norman Deakin made about *Spray*, which was built by Gill of Rochester 1902, on the lines of the original boat built by Slocum. *Spray* is very well known to me, having been owned successively by Dr. A. Haltermann, of Hamburg, Herr F. Behncke and Herr Leisegang of Berlin, who owns her still and has renamed her *Heimat*. I inspected this boat a couple of years ago and found her absolutely sound." [4]

Herr Leisegang told me that he bought the vessel in 1925. She was then called *Drei Rosen* (Three Roses), and, not being aware at that time of the *Spray*'s fame, he renamed her *Heimat* (Home). He wrote: "The *Heimat* was originally called *Spray* —a bell with the name on it was still on board—and, I have

102

been told, was built in England with three similar ships for a Pacific expedition. She was rigged as a gaff yawl, with a tiny mizzen of about 20 sq. metres. Altogether she had a sail area of 175 sq. metres with topsail."

According to Leisegang, the keel was deeper than the original *Spray*, and extended about three feet below the hull. It carried iron ballast, and there was also some inside ballast. He and his wife lived aboard the boat during the summer months and each year sailed her on the Baltic. One year, he chartered her out to a crew of students who sailed her to Bergen in Norway. He wrote later: "Unfortunately, I had to sell the ship in 1930, to Dr. Sharnowski of Poland, as I lacked money. I have never seen *Heimat* again, although in the succeeding years I sailed a lot on the Baltic. . . . She does not seem to be in Germany, for then I would probably have heard or seen something of her." Queried further about the three "similar" ships supposed to have been built at the same time as the Rochester *Spray*, Leisegang said he understood that they were sister ships. Could it have been that four vessels were built on the *Spray*'s lines at Rochester in 1902? So far no other information has been obtained.

In a letter to the editor of *Yachting World*, Wlodzimierz Glowacki, president of the Polish Yacht Association, wrote:

I have just read in Yachting World (September 1959, page 358) about the copies of Slocum's *Spray*. One of these copies, built in 1902 by Gill, in Rochester "is" owned, as you write in Yachting World, by Herr Leisegang of Berlin, and called *Heimat*. She is probably the same *Heimat* which had been bought on 26-6-1930 in Stettin by two Polish yachtsmen dr. Cz. Czarnowski and J. Fischer, who changed her name into *Jurand*. As *Jurand* this Rochester-copy of *Spray* had been bought in 1935 by the Akademicki Zwiazek Morski (Students Sea Association in Poland) and was in its use up to beginning of II World War. In September 1939, the *Jurand* was taken out on the shore and from this time we haven't had any information about her further fate, because, during the last war, the Nazi-Germans expelled Polish people from Gdynia. After the war we couldn't find any trace of *Jurand* and we presumed that she had been wrecked. . . .

103

The *Jurand* had a bell, with her first name *Spray* and, according to verbal tradition, she had been built in England for some scientific expedition into the polar waters before the I World War. She has about 180 sq. m. sails, yawl rigging.

First, a Pacific expedition, then a polar exploration—the Rochester *Spray*'s original purpose seemed to change over the years, but in any case, it had a rather romantic ring. Possibly the original owner did have intentions along such lines, but who would have believed that such a rumor could last so long or travel so far?

The passage in *Yachting World* referred to in the above letter contained a misprint; "is owned" should have been "was owned." Mr. Glowacki told me more about the *Jurand* in a letter:

Mr. Czeslaw Czarnowski, now living in Buenos Aires, who bought the *Heimat* from Mr. Leisegang in 1930 at Stettin (now Szczecin in Poland) made many voyages on the Baltic and North Sea with his partner Jan Fiszer. He changed the name *Heimat* to *Jurand*, the name of the hero in a book by Henryk Sienkiewicz, *The Teutonic Knights*. Mr Czarnowski, now 81 years old, was a very well known doctor, a good writer, and an excellent yachtsman. He wrote an interesting book about his voyages on the *Jurand*.

In 1936, if I remember well, the *Jurand* was bought by an organization of Polish Students called "Akademicki Zwiazek Morski" (Student Maritime Association). In September that year I sailed as first mate on her from Gdynia through Swinoujscie (Swinemuende) to Kopenhagen, Dragör (a little port near Kopenhagen), Ystad in Sweden and Roenne on Bornholm Island.

There were twelve of us aboard and although there was little place for us we enjoyed ourselves. The yacht was not designed for such a numerous crew but we arranged provisional berths: three in the forepeak and two in the afterpeak. Three berths were in the owner's cabin and three people slept in the mess. We rang the bell on which the name *Spray* was still engraved and we shared news about her glorious past.

I sailed three long trips on the *Jurand* before the war, each time for about one month. Her last trip under the Polish flag was made in August 1939. Since the beginning of the war I have never received any news about her till I got your letter.

A letter received from Herr Fritz Lescheck of Wedel-Holstein told about a yacht called the *Heimat* used by the Nazis in the war:

. . . the *Heimat* was appointed as training vessel for the Sea Rescue Patrol Service during the War. She was stationed at the sailing school of the Luftwaffe in Lobbe on the Rügen. During the last days of the war, she was used for the transport of refugees to Denmark. From here she went under tow to Schleswig, where she came under the care of the R.A.F., at their sea plane headquarters which was stationed there. This also happened to the other training ships of the Luftwaffe—*Seedrachen, Seewolf, Jungflieger,* and *Seestern.* The great majority of these boats were transported to England under tow in the summer of 1945, so that now one may also look there for the *Heimat.* Some boats stayed in Schleswig, but the *Heimat* was not among them.

On delivery, the *Heimat* was indeed not in sailing condition, but structurally still in good order. With adequate attention, she could still be in commission today.

Was the name *Heimat* merely a coincidence, or was this indeed the old Rochester *Spray?* It seems likely, as the sturdy nature and obvious seaworthiness of the vessel would have marked her out as eminently suitable for the Luftwaffe's purpose. Glowacki also thought so, and he wrote:

A few days before September 1st, 1939, nearly all our seagoing yachts were taken ashore in Gdynia harbour on the Baltic Sea. All Polish yachts were seized by German authorities in the first days of the Nazi occupation. They took them to different places in Germany and used them for their own purposes. So the information you received about the stay of the *Heimat* in Schleswig and its use by the Luftwaffe probably concerns our *Jurand.* I know too that many of Polish yachts were recognized after the end of the war as ours and given back to Poland by the British authorities in Germany or in the United Kingdom where some of them had been taken first . . . Perhaps the *Heimat* still exists and sails in the British waters under some new name.

Wilfried Trapp of Berlin sent me the plans of the *Heimat,* drawn by Andreas Kühl, naval architect of Hamburg. The basic measurements were here given as L.O.A. 53.7 feet, beam 14.1 feet, draft 5.9 feet.

THE *Ulula*

There was only one other English copy ever built. She was named the *Ulula* and, unlike the Rochester *Spray*, her present location is known.

Lloyd's Register for 1937 gave this information, "Auxilliary yawl, 2 cyl. paraffin motor, sails by McCready, 38' L.O.A. × 13.5' × 4', 5.75' headroom, 5.5' depth, designed by H. Allanson and built by Allanson & Son, Freckleton, in 1934." C. A. Rayner, commodore of the Portishead Cruising Club, knew the *Ulula* well, as her owner was an active member of the club. He wrote: ". . . her underwater lines are very similar to pictures of *Spray* which I have seen."

The owner, Charles Hinman, said: "She was built by G. J. Allanson & Son of Freckleton, Lancashire, in 1934 for a Blackpool Chemist who had won the Irish sweep and wanted a yacht like *Spray*." According to H. Allanson, present proprietor of the above firm, the chemist's name was Mr. Cook, and he has since died. Hinman continued:

I think the money must have run out before she was finished because Allanson built a most beautiful hull. Material and workmanship were first class. In the whole hull only one plank each side had a butt. All the rest ran the full length from stem to stern. But her spars were far too light, her sails were second hand and she had practically no internal fittings at all. She was fitted with a 15/18 h.p. Kelvin engine ten years older than herself.

The chemist kept her only a few months. He probably found he did not like sailing as she was very hard to handle in her first rig. Anyway she was sold twice in 1934. It is said that at one time that year or 1935 she was used to tow an illuminated sign advertising Littlewoods Football Pools off Blackpool Beach. When I bought her she had a large electric lighting set which subsequently lighted a twelve roomed house! Then Mostyn Williams bought her and brought her down to Bristol. He sailed her a few times but soon tired of her. Her engine was incorrectly tuned and so was hard to start. She had a wide flush deck with no protection for the helmsman, and the mainboom was so low that it actually touched the tiller as she tacked! The mizzen bumkin stuck out 13'6" over her stern and her bowsprit was even longer. It took two good men to sheet in her jib. Altogether a fair cow, and only one bunk below.

As you know, in our world of boats news of this kind travels very quickly and I soon heard that she was not everyone's dish, but one day I saw her out of water and was convinced that the hull was built to sail if properly rigged.

Well, I bought her—for a thousand pounds *less* than she had cost three years before. Having very little money and three children at the most expensive part of their education, I had to improvise and go slowly. The following were the jobs in the first winter: retune the engine—most successful, build two bunks and lockers in forecastle and the same in main cabin, abolish bumkin, shorten bowsprit by five feet, cut off foot of mainsail, make new main boom, cut jib-headed mizzen out of old lugsail, buy new staysail and jib, build deckhouse over engine room and steering cockpit. In 1938 and '39 she sailed; rather poorly looking with her shabby sails but she sailed well. . . .

On the eve of the outbreak of war, 2nd Sept. '39, I was ordered to Gloucester to take up my wartime job. I sailed up, unrigged *Ulula* and lived in her for the next ten months. During the war I was allowed some petrol and vapourizing oil so that I could use her for an occasional inspection trip up the Severn to Stourport (our waterhead), which is only nineteen miles from Birmingham. After the war my surviving son and I decided to shift the mizzen mast further forward turning her from a yawl into a ketch. This meant a new mizzen mast, gaff and boom. At the same time I gave her a complete new suit of sails, and wheel steering.

She knew every little port and anchorage in the Bristol Channel and up the Severn to Stourport.

The *Ulula* is now in Ireland and belongs to an officer of the Irish Navy.

THE *Pandora*

Six years after the building of the Rochester *Spray*, another copy was well on the way to completion on the other side of the world. The second vessel in this already growing *Spray*

fleet was the *Pandora*, built in Perth, West Australia. She became one of the best known copies, being the first small boat
to sail around Cape Horn. A Perth publication had this to say
about the building: "George McCarter is now engaged on an
interesting vessel for Mr. F. B. Blythe. She is being built to
sail round the world and her owner has adopted the design of
the famous yacht *Spray* as being the most suitable. She is 37 ft.
O.A. with a beam of no less than 14 ft. She is planked with
1¼" jarrah laid on jarrah keel, the ribs are bent timbers of
blackwood and stringybark built in three pieces each. As may
be judged she is unusually roomy and her career will be watched
with interest." [5]

H. Rumble of Perth provided more information:

I knew this boat very well and often visited McCarter's shed
during her construction. I understood she was an exact replica
of Captain Slocum's *Spray* . . . from my own observations at the
time, her construction seemed to be according to the original lines
of *Spray* as published in Capt. Slocum's book. The *Pandora* was
heavily built of jarrah and as far as I recall had all inside ballast.
She was launched and had her trial trip to Bunbury and return
under the name *The Distant Shore* but experienced some troubles—
the nature of which I cannot recall. Apparently Capt. Blythe
considered the name was unlucky—I was told that at the time—
and he thus changed it to *Pandora*. I remember he advertised
in the "West Australian" for a partner to sail around the world,
as a result of which a Capt. Arapakis joined him in the venture.

I am the oldest active sailing member of the Royal Perth Yacht
Club but I can now locate no old yachtsmen who were sailing
with me at the time *Pandora* was built or who I recall were well
acquainted with Geo. McCarter the boat builder—all seem to have
passed on. My sailing dates back for some years before *Pandora*'s
construction and although all my spare time has been spent on
the water I never saw *Pandora* under sail! For years I have been
Hon. Registrar and Measurer of Yachts for R.P.Y.C. but we have
no records of *Pandora*. Capt. Blythe seemed a man who kept to
himself and had nothing to do with my Club, the oldest in W.A.,
nor I think with any other Club. His boat seemed to quietly
disappear from Perth waters after spending a short period fitting
out at anchor off McCarter's shed.

The Perth correspondent of the Australian magazine *Seacraft*, J. R. Sharples, wrote me: ". . . the yacht you refer to was built in Perth by the late George McCarter and sailed from Fremantle with a quantity of blue metal for ballast. After leaving Fremantle the crew had to call in at Mandurah, a small estuary down the coast, in order to make a few adjustments, one of which could have been shifting ballast. From this point the yacht was then sailed to the Eastern States where their world cruise must have started."

The *Pandora* sailed from Bunbury, Western Australia, on May 3, 1910, and arrived at Melbourne on May 29. One Melbourne newspaper carried the following account:

Recollections of the adventurous round-the-world voyages accomplished some years ago by the small sailing vessels *Spray* and *Tilikum*, both of which visited Melbourne, are revived by the similar expedition on which *Pandora*, a 9-ton yawl, is about to embark. *Pandora*, which is slightly smaller than Captain Slocum's *Spray*, is constructed on much the same principle as that vessel, which, naturally, she closely resembles. Built in Western Australia within the past twelve months, *Pandora* will, it is claimed, be the most diminutive craft that has ever attempted a cruise around the world, and, consequently, her movements will be watched with considerable interest. She arrived in Hobson's Bay yesterday, after a stormy passage from Bunbury, Western Australia, during which she had about 6 feet of her port bulwarks washed away by heavy seas in the Great Australian Bight. She left the West Australian port on May 3d, and has therefore been twenty-six days in accomplishing the trip.

During the next fortnight *Pandora* will remain at moorings off Williamstown, where she will, no doubt, form an object of attraction. From this port she proceeds to Sydney, thence to New Zealand, Pitcairn Island, Easter Island, Juan Fernandez, the Falkland Isles, and the United States of America. Subsequently the small vessel will sail across the North Atlantic Ocean to England, and return to Australia by way of the Cape of Good Hope. *Pandora* is owned by Captain G. D. Blythe, of Coventry, England, who will accompany the yawl on her long cruise, having as a companion Captain Pietro Arapakis. *Pandora* a staunchly built vessel, is only 36 feet 9 inches in length over all, having a breadth of 14 feet 1 inch and a depth of 4 feet 1 inch.[6]

Incidentally, these measurements are exactly the same as Slocum's *Spray*, and thus refute the earlier statement that the *Pandora* was smaller.

The *Pandora* stayed at Melbourne for six weeks. On July 10 she sailed for Sydney and arrived at that port on August 16. The next day she left for Auckland, New Zealand. Foul weather was encountered on the Tasman crossing and the little vessel had a bad time. She stayed at Auckland for almost a month so that the damage suffered in the storm could be repaired, then headed away for Pitcairn and thence to Easter Island. A week ashore gave the navigators time to inspect the giant statues for which the island is famous.

From Easter Island the yawl sailed for Cape Horn, passing it on January 16, 1911. A week later she almost met disaster when struck by a huge wave that rolled her completely over. A Norwegian whaling vessel was met with soon after, which towed her into the Falkland Islands where repairs were effected. Later, the *Pandora* crossed to St. Helena, and then Ascension Island, before starting for New York, where she arrived June 23, 1911, having taken just 13 months and 20 days for the trip of over 22,000 miles.

From New York, the *Pandora* was bound across the Atlantic for London but, alas, she never reached another port. After leaving New York, nothing further was ever heard of the brave little vessel or her crew.

THE *Shamrock*

While the *Pandora* was in Melbourne, a *Spray* enthusiast, T. A. Dickson of Geelong, looked over her and went for a short sail. Some years later, he designed and had built a yacht based on *Spray* lines. His son, A. Stanley Dickson, wrote:

I am also enclosing five snaps of the *Shamrock*, a fine seagoing yacht which Dad had built in Geelong about 1915–16. The design of this was drawn up by himself and he incorporated in it the amidship section of the *Spray*.

The *Shamrock* left Victorian waters early in 1930. During the war I have heard that she was copper plated and used by the Navy up North. She was seen by an old Sea Salt friend (who has since died) at Bobbin Head, N.S.W., about four years ago (1957). I visited Bobbin Head in June of last year and had quite a search for the *Shamrock* without success. She may be of some interest to you if you can find her. Soon after the photographs enclosed were taken, her sails were changed to leg-o'-mutton.

So far no other information on this boat has been found.

THE ST. KILDA *Spray*

On his world voyage, Slocum stayed for quite some time at Melbourne, while waiting for favorable winds. The *Spray* lay at St. Kilda, a southern suburb on Hobson's Bay, for nearly a month. While there, she naturally attracted much attention, and one man was so impressed with her that he had a copy built. In his biography, Victor Slocum referred to a Mr. Shaw getting the lines of the *Spray* and building a copy.[7]

Robert Jones, the son of the builder wrote:

My father, Mr. J. B. Jones, built the replica of Slocum's *Spray* for Mr. Shaw of Harvey Shaw and Drake & Co. It was built about 1926–27, and I worked on it with my father . . . it remained at our place on the Marebyrnong River behind the Flemington Racecourse for some time and was later on taken to St. Kilda by a nephew of Mr. Shaw. The boat was blown up under the St. Kilda pier in a westerly gale and badly damaged. I do not know what happened to it after this. Mr. Shaw senior never used the boat and died a few years after it was built.

Jones went on to tell how his father had trouble with the local youths invading the boat in the swimming season, ". . . he used the 'tack' remedy and, according to all reports, it was equally successful!"

G. Garnsworthy of Pymble wrote: "I well remember a boat named *Spray* which for a great many years was moored in

111

front of our home at Hobson's Bay, Williamstown. It was owned by a Mr. Shaw."

J. Savage, a boatbuilder in Williamstown, said: "The boat you refer to, named the *Spray*, is now, and has been, lying in our yard for three or four years. Its condition at the present time is not very good as it has been neglected for the last 10 or 12 years. . . . We have always been under the impression that it is a copy of the original *Spray*. My father used to say so and he knew Slocum when he was out here."

Victor Slocum's statement about Mr. Shaw getting the lines of the *Spray* could imply that these were taken off in Melbourne, thus making the St. Kilda *Spray* an exact replica of the original. This point would be of little importance were it not for the doubtful authenticity of the published lines. However, it turned out that the latter were in fact used in the building. The issue was clarified by the owner, the late K. B. Johnstone of Brighton, who wrote:

Your letter to hand re *Spray*. I have since contacted Mr. Shaw Jnr. from whom I bought the boat some 20 years ago. He told me that his father had been dead about 25 years and that his affairs and estates had been wound up many years ago. The *Spray* was built by a Mr. Jones, as you say, from blueprints obtained we believe from America. Mr. Shaw says that Mr. Jones returned them.

The *Spray II* (mine) could not be a true copy of the *Spray* as she was altered to provide a 26" × 12" propeller aperture for an auxiliary engine. The *Spray* was smashed against Brighton pier in a 70–80 mile gale about 10 years ago. I started to repair her and at the same time lengthened her 7 ft., so her lines would be nothing like the original *Spray* now.

The present owner, Jack Read of Balwyn, Victoria, bought the St. Kilda *Spray* from Mr. Johnstone's estate and rebuilt and refitted her. After many years out of the water, the hull had opened up considerably and necessitated a complete re-caulking. However, the Huon Pine planking had stood up very well to the weather, with no checking or splitting. The hull was almost without any interior fittings at all in 1957, and Read has had to completely rebuild the accommodation. Masts, spars, and rigging had been stored away from the boat, but she is now completed and rigged as the original—a gaff ketch. However, there is no bowsprit, its place being taken by the seven-foot bow extension. A 30-horsepower diesel has been installed as an auxiliary motor. Mr. Read now sails the vessel on Port Phillip Bay.

THE *Chack Chack*

A vessel which was roughly based on the lines of the *Spray*, was built in Vancouver, British Columbia in 1924, by L. H. Roberts. She was a 12-ton gaff yawl, 36 feet by 11 feet 3 inches by 4 feet, with a hard chine. The freeboard amidships was 6 inches greater, and at the stern 10 inches greater than that of the *Spray*. The frames were 4-by-2-inch fir, about 20 inches apart, and the boat was planked with 1-inch cedar. An 8-horsepower single-cylinder auxiliary engine was fitted. Roberts and his wife lived aboard the vessel for several years and cruised extensively on the coast of British Columbia. Some delightful stories by Mrs. Roberts of *Chack Chack*'s wanderings were published in *Rudder* for January and December 1928, January and October 1929, and June 1931.

In one issue of *Rudder*, Roberts told about the building of the *Chack Chack*.

The germ started from my reading an account of the "Dream Ship" that sailed from England to the South Seas. Why not build a Dream Ship myself, something different from anything I had done before?

I went into my small sawmill and began looking over my stock of lumber on hand. That piece of fir, 6 by 12 by 26 feet, would be just the thing for the keel. And I could get the frames from that pile of 3 by 12's. That pile of clear red cedar, that I had been keeping for just such an unforeseen use, would plank her. I could already see my Dream Ship.

Taking a piece of beaver board, I drew up a set of lines for a 36 by 12 by 4 feet, V. bottom."

The underwater body I modelled as closely as possible after Captain Slocum's old *Spray*, carrying that wide waterline right

113

back to the stern, also the wide shoulders that give her an undeniably "skookum" appearance.

I gave her a little more freeboard and a little less beam than *Spray*, but even at that, she reminds one of a fat, black Siwash duck, squatting complacently upon the water.

Tucked under the thick jibboom is the carved likeness of a baldheaded eagle, its big cruel eyes and wicked yellow beak making it a splendid figurehead. From this figurehead comes her new name, *Chack Chack*, meaning "bad eagle" in Chinook.[8]

The fate of the *Chack Chack* during the next twenty years or so is little known. The only information has been supplied by George Riley of Vancouver, who wrote: "About 1928–29 Roberts was trying to sell her at a bargain price and left her picture etc. in every boatyard, ship chandler and broker's office in Coal Harbor. . . . Rumor said she was slow, unstable and had other unladylike attributes. During her life some wag named her *Odamit*, which seems, according to her reputation, very appropriate. She has since reverted to her original name *Chack Chack*. The boat was laid up for years in Coal Harbor, a sorry looking mess."

The *Chack Chack* story was brought up to date by John T. Dixon of New Westminster, who was the owner in 1960. He wrote:

Received your letter regarding the *Chack Chack* and it is very interesting to know that somebody (especially on the other side of the world) is interested in her.

I cannot say that I am a boat expert, but somehow in 1955 I became interested in boats. One day I happened to see an old hull high and dry on the sand and much against the owner's will he sold it to me—just the hull and water tank. My idea was to rebuild it but knowing nothing about boats I started inquiring around the waterfront and one day finally met an old fellow that used to own her for about 15 years. When I told him that I paid 30 dollars for her, the price really startled him and he said, "If you only paid 30 dollars for the *Chack Chack* I don't want to see it; that was one of the finest boats on the coast." He said that he had sailed her to China once and several times to Alaska.

114

Anyway, I rigged an outboard onto it and pushed it up the Frazer River so that it would be closer to home. I had it tied up to the wharf but the spring freshets were running so I had to move it. Its new mooring position was evidently in the way of some logging tugs and, as I could not be found, the Harbour Commission had her sunk in the middle of the river. Thereby went my dreams of having a good, safe, wide, comfortable sail boat.

Rather an ignominious end, this, to what was once a man's dream ship. That trip to China sounds interesting; I wonder how much truth there was in it?

THE *Little Spray*

It is rather fitting that the first American copy of the *Spray* was designed and built by the author of that now-famous analysis of the old vessel in the June 1909 *Rudder*, Cipriano Andrade, Jr. He told about his boat—a smaller version of the original—in *Fore An' Aft* magazine:

In the winter of 1908, 1909 I made as complete a technical analysis of the *Spray* as I could devise. A few years after that, my old friend Nutting asked me to build my next boat as a duplicate of the *Spray*.

So in the fall of 1918 I began a design of the *Spray* exactly like the original *Spray*, but with all dimensions just two-thirds of the original *Spray*, and with auxiliary power, and an iron keel. By the summer of 1920 this little duplicate of the *Spray* was finished and in the water. She amply justified my faith in the original.[9]

The *Little Spray* was rigged as a gaff sloop.

THE *Modified Spray*

Despite Andrade's original declaration in his analysis that the *Spray* was the "perfection" of her type, and his apparent satisfaction with the *Little Spray*, he went on to design a 25-foot boat which he called the *Modified Spray*. This had a vertical stem and no bowsprit, and apart from a gaff mainsail and a similar midship section, bears no resemblance at all to the *Spray*. The design, however, led to a most interesting exchange of opinions on the *Spray* and this boat in *Fore An' Aft*, and this alone makes the craft worth mentioning here.

Andrade led off with an article on his new design:

. . . in this design I have tried to closely follow all of the real essentials of the *Spray* in exact proportion. The displacement is practically the same. The draft is the same. The midship section is very nearly the same. The position and height of the mast is practically the same. The mainsail is almost the same. . . .

In the *Spray* the bottom of the keel at the bow is deeper than in this design, and the bottom of the keel at the stern is the same in both. The result is that in the *Spray* the keel is more nearly level fore and aft than in this design. The result of this is that the *Spray*, with her admirable light draft, suffers considerably more leeway than this design when working to windward. This difference in the pitch of the keel also sets the centre of lateral resistance of this boat further aft than in the *Spray*, and thereby permits the elimination of the bowsprit, so that the centre of effort also comes further aft than in the *Spray*. . . .

Also the vertical stern on this design is better than the angular stern on the *Spray*, because when under power, or even when running free under sail at a good speed, the water draws way up on the angular stern of the *Spray*, thus creating a constant suction and drag against her forward motion. This difficulty is entirely eliminated in the present design, which permits the water to flow free from the stern without any drag.[10]

The well-known naval architect, the late John G. Hanna, of Dunedin, Florida, took great exception to Andrade's statements. In the next issue of *Fore An' Aft*, he let fly with one of his typical—and entertaining—counterblasts:

For many years I have been an admirer of the little sloop in which Capt. Joshua Slocum circumnavigated the globe, and an indefatigable student of the whys, wherefores, and possibilities of the design. I have read with close attention everything on the subject that has been published, including Mr. Andrade's remarks in the June issue of this magazine. As a friend of the original design, I cannot permit some of his very far-fetched conclusions and un-

116

supported assertions to go unchallenged. I have no criticism to make of Mr. Andrade's latest design, in itself. . . .

What I object to is simply the allegation that this new craft, resembling not at all *Spray* but suggesting a cross between a Cape Cod cat, a river work-launch and a Dutch hoogarts—with apologies to Holland—is much superior to *Spray* in her own field. In other words, that *Spray* is inferior. . . . The friends of the defendant, poor old *Spray*, now accused of inferiority by the very man once her greatest admirer, have a right to be heard in her behalf.

Firstly, I deny emphatically that Mr. Andrade's latest pet is entitled to be called a modified *Spray*, or any kind of *Spray* at all. . . . His first claim is that "he has tried to follow all the real essentials of the *Spray* in exact proportion." He says the displacement is practically the same. But that is not an essential. One can hold to a displacement of 10,866 lbs. and yet on that design dozens of utterly different hulls including the worst kinds ever floated. He says the draft is the same. But that in itself is not an essential. There are tens of thousands of boats with the same extreme draft. The essential requirement for similarity in draft is that *every* point anywhere on the hull should in its draft (or depth below waterline plane) bear a fixed and definite mathematical relationship to the corresponding point on *Spray*'s hull. This is far from being the case. Next, it is claimed that the position and height of the mast is practically the same, and one infers the mast is to be greased with the same grade of tallow Slocum used, as this would be an equally important point of similarity. The mainsail is also claimed to be almost the same. But a boat does not live by her mainsail alone, unless she is a cat; the whole sail plan must be considered for any claim of similarity, and so we see at once that any claim in similarity of rig falls as flat as plate glass. . . . The rig on the newest boat is so nearly a cat that it certainly cannot be claimed better than *Spray*'s for real sea use, however . . . and its center of effort is entirely too far aft, judged by the unanimous opinion of all small-boat sailors. It is well known that the small boat must have her center of area well forward of her center of lateral plane. . . .

Next, let us examine the claim that *Spray* "suffers considerably more leeway than this design when working to windward" because the angle of the keel has been increased in the new design. What is the actual increase? I measured it. *Spray*'s keel angle is 2 degrees. The new boat's angle is 3 degrees. Do you believe, long-

117

suffering reader, that the infinitesimal and absurd difference of 1 degree is going to make "considerable difference in leeway?" Neither does your old man, I'll bet. The truth is, a 25-foot *Spray* model of 3-foot draft makes worse leeway than a 36-foot *Spray* model of 4-foot draft, for the well-known reason that small craft must have *relatively more*, not *proportionately the same*, draft as larger boats, if we expect equally good performance. You can't ever alter this fundamental law by juggling any keel angle one degree. . . .

Next, there is the claim that "the vertical stern on this design is better than the angular stern of the *Spray*, because . . . the water draws way up on the angular stern of the *Spray*, thus creating a constant suction and drag against her forward motion. This difficulty is entirely eliminated in the present design, which permits the water to flow free from the stern without any drag."

That last statement is one sure to bring roars of laughter from all naval architects who have specialized in power-boat design. They have had the truth pounded into them by twenty years of grief that absolutely the only way to make water break free from a transom stern is to bring the transom right flat down on the water and even under the water. They know that the sharper the curvature of buttocks and diagonals aft, the more water is going to be dragged upward—or the boat will drag downward. . . . It is evident that in the new design there is more curvature to buttocks and diagonals aft than in the old, consequently more, and not less, drag can be expected. It is the whole weight of water dragged by the whole after half of hull, and not the bucketful of froth that recurves against a small area of immersed transom, that holds a boat back. . . .

Finally, I want to note an exception to the claim that a bowsprit is not a real necessity. The disadvantages of a bowsprit are so obvious that mankind would have quit using it long ago if it were not absolutely necessary . . . the longer a man has sailed and studied the real how and why of sail propulsion, the more certainly he realizes that the sail plan must be extended forward of the body of any normal boat. This is best done by a spar; it can also be done, if you have money to waste, by building on a very long, thin extension of the bow, sticking out in the air far beyond the real immersed body of the craft. This is nothing more nor less than a bowsprit, and serves the same purpose. . . .

So much for this particular design. By way of constructive

criticism I would like to say something on the general subject of modifying *Spray*—or any design. I hold still to the belief Andrade once held and thoroughly proved—that her peculiar merit as a single-hander was in her remarkable balance of all effective centers of effort and resistance on her midship section line. This merit he has completely thrown to the dogfish in his alteration. Yet the *Spray* lines can be modified to any degree of fineness desired without losing this characteristic. It is only necessary that the modification be made by strict mathematical formula applied to every dimension. Two or three formulae may be used together and they may be simple or complex, but as long as they are applied consistently the resulting hull will have similarity of line, identity of centers and the same *qualitative* characteristics, however much the quantitative may vary." [11]

In the following issue of the magazine, Andrade replied at length, justifying his design and criticizing Hanna's remarks. However, the points made dodged the real issues Hanna raised, and in any case are of little interest here.

THE *Faith*

In the September *Fore An' Aft* article, John Hanna gave the lines of his own modification of the *Spray*.

Published herewith are lines of a modified *Spray* I drew for a large vessel. Her outside proportions are conventional for her size. As nearly everyone knows, large craft must have relatively less beam than small ones. The formulae of modification were very complex, and to be sure of results I checked measurements of principal centers, finding that they came out on the midship section line for this hull just as exactly as they do on the original *Spray*. She should be as well balanced, as easy to handle, as capable of handling herself, as was Slocum's boat. Moreover, she should also sail at a small angle of heel, for this is a characteristic that depends on the balance between upsetting and righting forces, and while she has relatively less righting force than the beamy *Spray*, she still has the characteristically powerful *Spray* section and a sail plan that has a relatively lower center of pressure, and so less upsetting force. Like *Spray*, her sailing angle should be about 10 degrees.[12]

119

The length of this vessel was not mentioned and no scale rule was shown with the lines. However, in view of Hanna's statement that she was large, the lines published were almost certainly those of the 87-foot ketch *Faith*, the largest copy of the *Spray* ever built. This vessel was referred to in an article called "Yachts of the Movie Stars" by Stewart Robertson, in *Rudder*.

Boat-owning motion picture producers include John Ford, whose eighty-seven foot ketch *Araner* (formerly *Faith*) was designed by Hanna on the lines of Captain Slocum's famous *Spray*. She was built in Essex, Massachusetts, in 1926 and takes the palm for distance covered. She has twice made the 5,000-mile round trip to the Hawaiian Islands, has been once to Acapulco, Mexico, and back, 2,500 miles, and makes the 2,000-mile round trip to the Gulf of California every year. Like most Southern California vessels she is kept in commission all the year around, and her owner uses her for weekends during the all too brief intervals from the studio grind.[13]

THE *Foam*

Some years prior to his article in *Fore An' Aft*, John Hanna had designed another modification of the *Spray*, which he called the *Foam*. Although many yachtsmen admire the performance of the old *Spray*, there were several things about her which discourage them from having an exact copy. Chief among these were her great beam, shoal draft, and lack of outside ballast. Hanna remedied this in his *Foam* design, which he dealt with in detail in *Motor Boat:*

For many years I have stood second only to Mr. Cipriano Andrade Jr. as a student and admirer of *Spray*. . . . Could *Spray* be altered so as to bring her within limits a yachtsman would consider, and yet keep strictly to her characteristic form and preserve as far as possible her marvellously perfect balance, as proved by Andrade's analysis of all her centers? This question was so alluring that I dusted off the old drawing board at once, grabbed a pencil, and was unable to let go for 22 hours.

120

The changes were not made with the idea of improving on the *Spray*, but rather, in Hanna's own words, ". . . to make all necessary concessions to the fashion of our day. . . ."

I ask that it be especially noted that I have made no attempt to "improve" the lines anywhere by altering their character, nor their dimensions a hair's breadth otherwise than as imposed by the requisite narrowing of the hull, all of which was done in strict proportionality.[14]

Roger Strout, owner of the *Igdrasil*, confirmed Hanna's alterations as being mainly social concessions. He wrote: "I had considerable correspondence with Hanna after my first cruise so I can state positively that his reason for reducing the beam was purely social. He was well aware that the 14 foot beam would not be well received in most yacht clubs. He was right."

Three years after Hanna's article appeared, the *Foam* was built. The vessel is still in existence today, and her present owner is Horace W. Schmahl of New York, who renamed her the *Island Trader*. Mr. Schmahl wrote:

I thought you might be interested in knowing about another copy of the *Spray*. I own this vessel. She was built as the *Foam* in Tonowanda on Lake Ontario by George Reid Richardson in 1926. . . . Through the cooperation of our Coast Guard, which is always glad to get into the act when it comes to preserving our marine tradition, I was able to complete my research into the antecedents and the identification of the previous owners of the *Island Trader*. Since then, I have also been in touch, both telephonically and in writing, with all but two of the previous owners or their next of kin and, again with the help of the various Coast Guard officers in Cleveland, New London, etc., have been able to obtain very early photographs of the *Island Trader*.

The first owner of record was a Mr. Matthew H. Knapp of New York. I called Mr. Knapp but found that he had gone on a trip to the north woods. A few days ago I received a letter from Mrs. Knapp advising me that her husband had suffered a stroke and therefore was unable to reply personally to my letter. However, he dictated a brief note to Mrs. Knapp and attached a number of photographs of the vessel, including one showing her rigged as a brigantine. From what I have learned through Mr. Knapp, the *Island Trader*, or *Foam*, was originally designed and built for a Dr. Harvey Slocum, a physician who lived in New York and who claimed some distant relationship to Capt. Joshua Slocum. The vessel was rigged as a sloop like the *Spray*. Dr. Slocum evidently met with some financial reverses and was unable to complete the construction of the vessel. Mr. Matthew H. Knapp, who was a wealthy landowner and an old schooner captain, saw the boat and bought her. However, he decided to rig her as a tops'l schooner with a large square yard. In the United States, vessels of this type are frequently misnamed "brigantines." With this rig, Mr. Knapp sailed the vessel for many years on the Great Lakes and eventually via the Erie Canal to the Atlantic seaboard and down to the Bahamas, Virgin Islands, etc. I am sending you a copy of an old photograph showing the vessel as she was rigged under the ownership of Mr. Knapp. Another photograph shows her as a tops'l schooner under full sail replete with working jib and flying jib. You will recognise the two cabin houses of the old *Spray* design. Incidentally, the sailor attired in white gear who can be seen standing slightly aft of the main mast is none other than the late John Foster Dulles, the first Secretary of State under President Eisenhower, who, for many years, was a crewman on the *Foam* when she was sailing on the Great Lakes.

According to Coast Guard records, the *Foam* was sold to Knapp in April 1936. In 1944 she was sold again, and since then has had eight owners in New York and Connecticut, until July 1960, when purchased by Mr. Schmahl. At present, the vessel is on her way around the world with Schmahl and his family aboard.

THE *Sagamore*

A neighbor of Mr. Knapp, seeing his *Foam*, wanted a vessel like it, but believed that strict adherence to the *Spray*'s midship section would be better. Hanna accordingly prepared for him the *Foam II* design, more similar to the *Spray* than his first modification. The boat was built, and actually proved to be the superior vessel, so plans for *Foam I* were retired. Since then, *Foam II* plans have been sold to many people and quite a number of vessels in various parts of the world have been built to them. In a letter written in 1944, Hanna stated that eight boats had been built from the plans. Since then, others have also been constructed. *Foam II* is certainly the best known and probably the most satisfactory of all modifications of the *Spray*.

One well-known *Foam* is the *Sagamore*, built in 1939 at Balboa, Canal Zone, by Captain Elmer B. Small, a retired Panama Canal pilot. Her keel and stem were of Central American hardwood, the planking of cypress, and the deck teak. Small and his son built her themselves, with native help for some of the major items such as framing and planking. The vessel was launched in the fall of 1940, but after fitting out, had time only for a shakedown cruise before she was requisitioned by the Army for coastal patrol duty. Eventually, Captain Small repurchased her, and after repairing and refitting, cruised extensively around the northern shore of South America and among the islands of the West Indies, before going north through the Inland Waterway to New York. Captain Small was killed in an auto accident several years ago. His son, Neal E. Small, keeps the *Sagamore* in Mill Basin, Brooklyn, where he is refitting her.

THE OXFORD *Spray*

A copy which has become very well known on the eastern coast of the United States was built by Captain R. D. Culler at Oxford, Maryland, in 1929. The plans used for her building were specially prepared for Culler by Victor Slocum, who scaled up the lines in *Sailing Alone Around the World*. Her keel and 6-by-8-inch sawn frames were oak, and she was planked with 1½-inch Georgia pine. She was ceiled and salted in old coaster style, carrying a ton of salt. This served a threefold purpose—pickling and thus preserving the wood, keeping the bilge sweet, and absorbing moisture, leaving a dry cabin. A 40-horsepower auxiliary engine was fitted. The original sail plan was used, with the addition of a topsail, which came in

123

handy when sailing in the light summer airs on Chesapeake Bay, where the *Spray* spent a lot of time. She was rigged in the traditional style of the trading coasters on the U. S. eastern seaboard, and was in fact actually used to several years to carry freight on the Chesapeake. Captain Culler and his wife owned her for twenty-three years, during which time she was their home, and for nineteen years, their business, as they used her for charter cruises. She proved very satisfactory for this purpose.

Mrs. Toni Culler wrote about the vessel in *Rudder:*

Pete, my husband, was and is a Slocum enthusiast. At the age of sixteen he bought a pair of brass Navy bow chocks from an old Scotchman on the west coast. He knew that some day his *Spray* would be built around these. Pete's enthusiasm went one step further than most. He recognized in Slocum's exploits not only his amazing seamanship but also his wisdom in choosing a model of a boat which would be seaworthy, comfortable, and workable for extended cruising anywhere. Ten years ago, after eighteen months of the hardest and most satisfying work in the world, he completed his ship and she slid down the ways into the water, the chocks in place on the bow.[15]

Captain Culler himself wrote me: "I've always been interested in self steering, which is one of the reasons why I built the *Spray* model."

While owned by Culler, the *Spray* cruised extensively on the east coast and inland waterways; headquarters for the spring and fall were in Chesapeake Bay. She headed north to Maine for the winter and south to Florida for the summer.

The *Spray* was sold in 1952 and has changed hands frequently since then. The second owner fitted her up with all manner of gadgets and electronic equipment—as one advertisement offering her for sale in September 1956 termed it: "everything Slocum wished he had." At that time, her inventory included "a Red-wing 4-cylinder, 65-horsepower Diesel engine, two Monel metal fuel tanks (240 gallons), 1500-watt petrol generator, one set 32 volt batteries, complete heating system, two Monel water tanks, built-in S/S lined electric refrigerator, four-burner S/S gas range, chrome folding lavatory, hand and electric toilet,

124

radio direction finder, radio-telephone, depth sounder, photo-electric pilot, Edson steering gear, electric windlass, speed-ometer, five foam mattresses, three plate-glass mirrors, wall-to-wall carpeting, and remote control fire extinguishing system."

As boats go, copies of the *Spray* are few and seem, like rare stamps, to command rather good prices. The Oxford *Spray* was set at $15,000.

The latest owner is Dr. Charles Johnson of Massachusetts. In June 1961, he and his wife left Boston and sailed the vessel to the Azores, Madeira, and Canaries, and back across the Atlantic to the West Indies—an 8000-mile cruise.

THE *Basilisk*

In the year following the building of the Oxford *Spray*, the keel of another copy was laid down at the same yard. This was in fact built from the same set of lines as the former vessel. Keel and frames were of white oak, planking of Georgia pine, and cabin and decking of white cedar, with Oregon pine masts and spars. Named the *Basilisk*, after a West Indian lizard that has the ability to run across the surface of the water, she was constructed specially for a scientific expedition to the West Indies sponsored by the American Museum of Natural History. The *Basilisk* was fitted out as a floating laboratory, with instrument table, library, refrigerator, and complete photographic facilities, as well as living quarters and stowage space. The type of craft required was outlined in the museum's journal, *Natural History*.

"A boat was needed that would be seaworthy, comfortable to live in, staunch, yet small enough for one or two men to handle in any weather. It must be able to carry water for a period of several months, and provisions for at least half a year, and yet allow space to work and live." [16] The requirements were thus rather exacting, but after much consideration it was decided that the expedition could do no better than duplicate the *Spray*.

The *Basilisk* was rigged like the original *Spray*, and had no engine. She was wrecked on Great Inagua Island in the Bahamas

125

on her first major voyage. The sails were salvaged, and later bought by Roger Strout, the owner of the *Igdrasil*. They were of 15 oz. canvas, and still in sufficiently good condition for Strout to use as far as Australia. Despite the loss of his ship, the owner, Gilbert C. Klingel, decided to remain on the island for a time after his companion on the voyage, W. Wallace Coleman, had returned home. In his book *Inagua* (*The Ocean Island*), he wrote an entrancing story of the voyage and the shipwreck, and his observations of the varied land and sea life of this lonely island. He also told how the *Basilisk* came to be modeled on the famous *Spray:*

As far back as I could remember I had dreamed of owning a sailing ship, a sleek thing of tall masts, of taut gleaming canvas and smooth white hull. It is a dream common to many men. . . .

The interlude began in the strange little Republic of Haiti where I was engaged in biological research for the American Museum of Natural History. . . . As the time came to return home came close I became interested in a research problem that made it desirable to visit a number of the other West Indian Islands, particularly some of the small uninhabited and less frequented ones.

It was the spell of these islands, lying low under the horizon, that drove the dream into reality. . . . Why not give up business, seek the islands in one's own ship, in a vessel fitted expressly for the purpose?

Such is the driving power of dreams that in due time we found ourselves with a snug little sailing ship, the backing of a great museum and an appalling sense of what we had started. But it was not as simple as that. A year and a half slipped by before we even found our ship. We did not just pick her up—our boat had to fill too many specifications. We needed a ship that would be seaworthy, staunch and sturdy. We had to have room in which to live and work in comfort; we had to be able to carry provisions and water for long periods so as to be independent regardless of location; we had to have a ship that could be sailed in any weather by one man, if necessary. Such a boat was not easy to find. We scouted all over our home waters, over the Chesapeake Bay. Nothing suited; all that we could find were too old, too narrow, too flimsy, too large or small—everything but what we wanted. Eventually, and unexpectedly, the search came to an end. In a small shipyard at Oxford, Maryland, in process of construction was exactly what we desired. Could we buy the vessel? We were told that we could not, for the owner also had his dreams, but that we could have one made like it. Within a month the contract was in the builder's hands.

We had chosen a famous model. In fact we had chosen one of the most famous boat models of all time. Our ship was to be an exact replica, except for the cabin and fittings, of the famous *Spray* of Captain Joshua Slocum who, it will be remembered, sailed the original around the world single-handed in the late 1890s. He set a precedent in maritime history and proved beyond all question that open ocean sailing in small boats was both practical and safe. All honor to him. As time proved, if we had searched the world over we could not have selected a better model.[17]

THE *Igdrasil*

One of the best-known copies of the *Spray* was the *Igdrasil*, built at Savannah, Georgia, in 1933 by Roger S. Strout, and sailed around the world by him and his wife from 1934 to 1937. The *Igdrasil* left Jacksonville, Florida, in June 1934, and sailed via the West Indies to the Panama Canal and into the Pacific Ocean. She called at the Galapagos, the Marquesas, the Tuamotus, Tahiti, Samoa, and Fiji before reaching New Zealand. The real object of the cruise had been to visit the Sounds of the southwest coast of the South Island, and after cruising extensively through this rugged and little-known region of New Zealand, the Strouts decided to continue the voyage westward. They crossed the Tasman Sea to Brisbane, sailed north inside the Great Barrier Reef, through the Torres Strait, and across the Indian Ocean to Durban, stopping at Christmas Islands, the Cocos, and Rodriguez. The *Igdrasil* sailed via the Cape of Good Hope to St. Helena and Ascension, and completed her circumnavigation by crossing the Atlantic to America.

In 1938 the vessel made a cruise to Alaska and return, 14,000 miles in ten months. She sailed by way of the West Indies, Panama Canal, and the Hawaiian Islands, and after exploring

127

the Alaskan seaboard, followed the coast down on her return south.

The *Igdrasil* was not an exact copy of the *Spray*, being slightly wider and deeper. Her dimensions were 37 feet by 33 feet by 14 feet 6 inches by 5 feet. She was constructed of pitch pine and white oak, and a 4-cylinder Miller petrol engine was fitted as auxiliary. Like the *Spray*, she was first rigged as a sloop, and a second mast added later on. So far, she has been the only copy to sail around the world. Roger Strout, in an article in *Yachting*, gave in detail his reasons for choosing the *Spray* design:

When I determined to try the glare of the sun on dancing waves, instead of on chromium plate along our dusty highways, I was totally devoid of those rabid prejudices one usually encounters among yachtsmen in favor of their local designs, for I had never owned or sailed anything larger than a canoe. This does not imply ignorance of boats, for I had spent much of my life on the coast of Maine and had seen boats, talked boats and felt on intimate terms with the working types up to the six-masted schooners they once turned out in the nearby city of Bath. With this background, I naturally approached ocean cruising with the idea of shrinking down a work boat model to meet requirements rather than strengthening up a yacht design.

I began my plans about the time the present spurt of ocean racing was getting into full swing. I admired the costly flyers and respected their records, but I did not envy their owners. Crossing the Atlantic in two and a half weeks is nice, if you can move ashore for a rest afterwards, but that isn't cruising. I felt then, and three years of continuous cruising has strengthened my conviction, that, though they are both great sports, ocean racing and ocean cruising have nothing in common except the ocean.

Seaworthiness, comfort and carrying capacity are the standards by which an ocean cruiser must be judged. . . . So the cruising man wants a small cargo boat design, polished up to look respectable under a yacht ensign!

When considering such designs one cannot avoid the broad, round-nosed, comparatively shallow type that was the ancestor of Captain Slocum's *Spray*. It has great carrying capacity, may be beached almost anywhere, is comfortable in the extreme, and the *Spray* proved that her utility is not confined to Dutch canals. A study of the record shows that the *Spray* was faster, on long passages, than any of the more modern one- or two-man boats. That clinched the argument; sentiment had nothing to do with it. . . . The general form is that of an eminently satisfactory craft and that was all that was wanted.[18]

In 1939, the *Igdrasil* was sold to D. Grant and L. Smith, who changed her name to *Tané* and planned to sail her to the South Pacific. However, their cruise did not go past Southern California.

The *Igdrasil* is now named the *Faith*, and is owned by Edwin L. King of Newport Beach, California. She was extensively refitted in 1957 and 1958, and a 42-horsepower Gray engine installed. In 1959 she was advertised for sale for $20,000. The inventory included: two new suits of sails, one light and one heavy, new blocks, S/S Porthole Pete wood and coal stove, foam rubber mattresses six inches thick, two anchor chains, three anchors, one anchor rode, radio receiver, aluminum dinghy, outboard motor, auxiliary generator, two water tanks totaling 100 gallons, and two gas tanks totaling 88 gallons.

THE *Starbound*

Victor Slocum's plans, used for the Oxford *Spray* and the *Basilisk*, served for yet another copy of the *Spray*. This was the *Starbound*, built in 1950 at Highlands, New Jersey, by J. Kenneth Whitteker, former Technical Editor of "The Rudder." She was an enlarged version, 62 feet by 18 feet by 6 feet, 31 tons gross, based on lines scaled up from the above-mentioned plans. The *Starbound* was rigged as a ketch with 1700 square feet of canvas in her five lowers. She also carried a flying jib, square sail, and raffee. The auxiliary engine was an 84-horsepower Diesel.

In 1957 the vessel was sold to the well-known folk singer Burl Ives, who renamed her the *Black Spoonbill*. She was stranded on Rehoboth Beach, Delaware, in October 1957, by a hired crew on a trip to Florida, but was towed off. She

129

was later bought by Louis C. F. Van Ael of Baltimore, who is refitting her at Annapolis.

THE MINNEAPOLIS *Spray*

A copy of the *Spray* was listed for sale in the November 2, 1958, issue of "The Marine Mart," Pageland, South Carolina. The advertisement read: "Exact copy of Josh Slocum's *Spray* built 1949, 40′ × 14.5′ × 4.5′, displacement 17 tons, double planked hull, oak frames in perfect condition. Almost new 40 h.p. Diesel engine. Needs cabin and deck work and mast. Marine survey this year estimates replacement cost at $30,000. No time to do necessary work, will sacrifice for $3,500. E. Bratton, 326 Ling-A-Mor Terrace, So., St. Petersburg, Fla. 75950."

In a letter, the owner, Eugene B. Bratton, gave the following information:

The *Spray* was built in 1949 at Minneapolis, Minn. It is a heavy built hull, steam bent oak frames on about 12″ centers size about 1½″ × 2″ with heavy sawn frames every 3′. Planking is 2 layers of ¾″ pine, iron fastened. To my knowledge, the hull is perfectly sound. The cabin and decks are very rough. I have removed practically all the interior of the cabin, leaving only the electric refrigerator, gas stove, and the toilet and water tanks. The cabin needs complete refinishing, as do the decks and the mast. The rigging is alright, and most of the blocks, etc., are with the boat. The sails are fair and are of very heavy canvas. The boat is documented and I have the hull insured for $4,500. Actually, the Red Wing Diesel engine is worth about $3,000, as it is almost new and is fresh water cooled. Captain Slocum's "Sailing Alone Around the World," which is available at most libraries, gives an accurate layout of her lines and some facts about her of a more detailed nature."

Early in 1957, Forrest B. Morgan, of Rhode Island, saw a copy of the *Spray* in St. Petersburg, Florida, which, he was told, was built in Wisconsin. Now, Minneapolis is not far from the Wisconsin border, and it seems almost certain from a description of the boat that it was in fact the one advertized for sale in St. Petersburg the following year. However, Mr.

130

Morgan's impressions were not quite as favorable as the owner's. He wrote:

There is a boat tied up in the marina in St. Petersburg, Florida, named the *Spray* which looks like the original and which the owner showed me. He stated the hull was built in Wisconsin by a boat builder on order by a retired railroad engineer on as close lines to the original *Spray* as possible. He finished off the cabin himself, mostly with Masonite, and it looks it. The boat was then sailed down to St. Pete or Tampa where it was sold. After passing through other hands it is now owned by a fisherman who put a fish hold in her and installed a small Red Wing diesel engine. Masts are in but no sails. The interior looks a mess but the hull appears sound. It is very bluff bowed and beamy. Makes me think of a Dutch canal boat. The owner wants $4,500 for it, if anyone is interested.[19]

In 1962, Mr. Morgan gave me some more particulars about this vessel: "I remember this boat *Spray* and tried to buy it, but above water it was rotten. A knife would go in three to four inches in many places. Masts were out and in poor shape. It would have needed a complete rebuilding although the shipyard man said she was sound below the water line. I have not been in St. Petersburg for some time but a friend said she had been moved and he could not find her."

THE *Spray* BY MASTERSON AND SCHLEGEL

One interesting modification of the *Spray* was a motor sailer designed by a New York firm. The dimensions were L.O.A. 41 feet 7 inches, L.W.L. 36 feet, Beam 12 feet 8 inches, Draft 5 feet. The sail area was 620 square feet. A short account of the boat appeared in *Yachting*.

Masterson and Schlegel, of New York, have done an interesting job of grafting a modern streamlined profile and an up-to-date rig onto a century-plus-old hull design, in this motor sailer. For her hull lines are those of the already-ancient sloop *Spray* in which Captain Joshua Slocum sailed around the world single-handed over half a century ago. Like her predecessor, she will be no racing yacht but should prove able and a good deal more

131

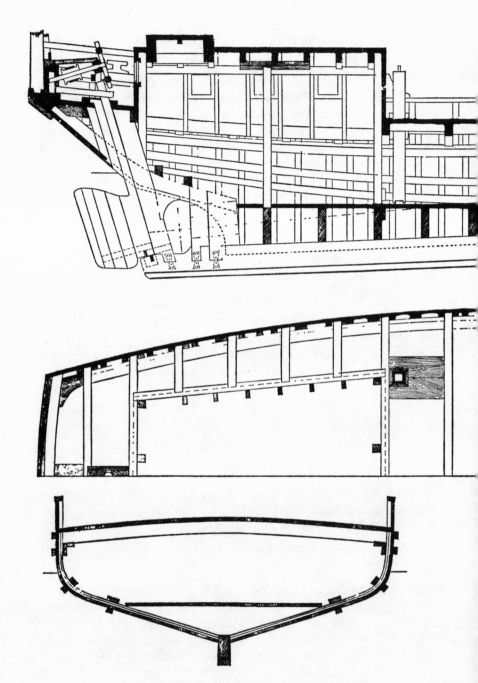

B. Construction Plans of the *Spray*

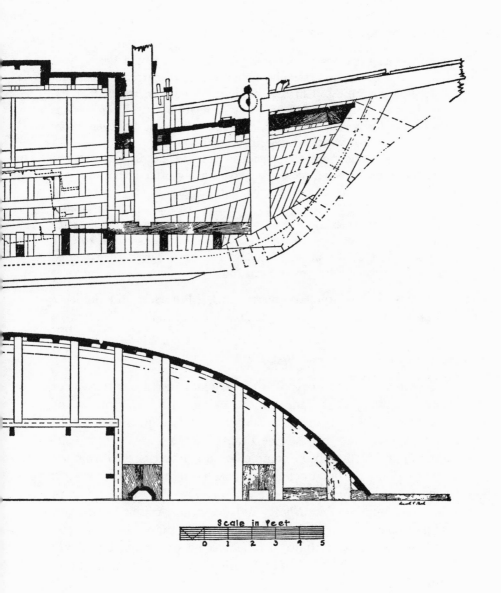

Scale in feet

0 1 2 3 4 5

Designed and drawn by Kenneth E. Slack, May 1962

comfortable than *Spray*. She has the old boat's broad beam, hard bilges and long keel which, unlike *Spray*'s, carries a 6000-lb. iron shoe. Her 8-cyl. Chrysler engine is a modern touch that the late Captain Slocum would probably have found handy on various occasions during his 46,000-mile cruise, and will be even more useful in this boat with her snug jib-headed sloop rig.

Her accommodations are spacious, with full headroom throughout. She will sleep five persons, two in a big after stateroom, one in a single forecastle, one in the big deckhouse and another on the dinette opposite the galley. She has loads of deck space and dual controls, steering either from the deckhouse or the after cockpit. In short, she looks like a comfortable vessel to live aboard either at sea or in port, and one well suited to extended off-shore cruising in fair weather or foul.[20]

A nice design going to waste, this; Masterson and Schlegel recently informed me that the boat was never built.

THE LOCKWOOD FOLLEY *Spray*

The unfortunate story of a copy which was built but never launched was told to me by the owner, Eric C. Squires, of New York. "My copy of the *Spray* was being built at Lockwood Folley, just behind the turn of Cape Fear, North Carolina. The hull had been completed, and I had already shipped a two-cylinder, four-cycle Fisherman's engine, when the small yard was afire by some local person who was 'feuding' with the boat builder. My *Spray* and six other vessels were lost. Thus was shattered a boyhood dream. On the rebound I married, so the idea of the *Spray* had to be put aside, but never forgotten. Perhaps some day I will be in a position to build another. . . ."

THE *Spray* BY EDWIN MONK

A modification of the *Spray* by the naval architect Edwin Monk of Seattle, Washington, appeared in *Rudder*. It was prepared for a Mr. Karl A. Shearer ". . . who wanted a family boat to sleep six in less than forty feet overall length and sug-

134

gested that the designer develop a modernized version of Captain Joshua Slocum's *Spray*. The boat carries no outside ballast and there is a world of room in her. She is 39 feet overall, 14 feet beam, and 4 feet 6 inches draft. Total sail area is 846 square feet." [21]

Mr. Monk himself provided me with more information: "We made two *Sprays*, both of them 39 feet long and 14 feet beam. The first one was a close replica but the second was deepened to 5 feet 4 inches draft, the thought being that a deeper boat would be a little better sea boat. This one has 3000 pounds of outside ballast. . . . We had only the small scale and rather rough lines in 'Sailing Alone Around the World' from which to work."

The second design was prepared for Evan King of Los Angeles.

Karl Shearer, Jr., wrote me: "Due to financial circumstances and the death of my mother, my father was not able to build his boat. Because of my interest in his project and my great love for the sea and sailing, my father has given me his plans, notes, etc., so that I may build the boat he was not able to build. At this time I am building a model of the boat to a scale of ¾ of an inch to a foot. By staying to the plans and specifications I hope to discover and remedy any mistakes or problems that may occur in the process of construction."

THE *Sirius*

One very recent copy of the *Spray* to be launched was built at Monkton, Vermont, by Robert W. Carr, from 1950 to 1956. The story of this vessel, named the *Sirius*, deserves telling, as it is a perfect example of how the words of the old captain have inspired people since to build replicas.

One day in 1936, Bob Carr was on shore leave from his navy ship going through the Panama Canal. Looking for some reading matter, he went into a public library in the city of Christobal. Here he happened to see a copy of Slocum's *Sailing Alone Around the World*. Fascinated, he read the entire book from cover to cover before leaving.

So was born the familiar dream of building a little ship and sailing in her to far-away shores. In contrast to most dreamers, Bob Carr was also a man of action, with the initiative and drive to make his dreams come true. In *Motor Boating*, Gordon P. Manning wrote about the *Sirius* and her beginnings:

The fabulous story of the original *Spray* enchanted this boy who had been born in Massachusetts, but brought up on the shores of the blue Pacific. . . . it was rather appealing—and particularly to a young man who loved the sea, and who loved old-fashioned sail the way Bob Carr did. "The idea came to me about a week later, that I would like to build myself an exact copy of *Spray*," Bob recalled. "I suppose it had been in the back of my mind ever since I had read about Joshua Slocum and his voyage. My Dad was a good carpenter, and I knew a little about tools, as I'd been brought up on a farm, and you learn a little about everything there. Captain Slocum told about going into the woods for young oak saplings for his frames, and I wanted to do the same thing when I built my boat. We had plenty of oak trees on the place, and I knew that would be no problem." [22]

The Second World War, however, interrupted Carr's plans, and he had to lay aside his dream while he went to sea again, this time in the Merchant Marine. After eight years of service, he retired to a hill farm near Monkton's Ridge, Vermont. Caring for over one hundred acres and twenty cows did not leave him much spare time, but that did not stop him from dreaming about the *Spray* and making plans.

It was in the summer of 1950 that the big project finally got under way. The building of this *Spray* is rather different from that of most others, for Bob Carr worked alone and fashioned his own little ship by hand. He went into the woods with his ax and felled his own oak trees for keel and frames, adzing them to shape in the age-old tradition of shipbuilding. For four years he worked, without the benefit of power tools or equipment, to make his dream come true. In addition to building the entire hull of *Sirius* alone, Bob Carr shaped her masts and spars, hand-sewed two complete suits of sails out of heavy canvas, and forged his own ironwork for the rigging fittings. The keel and steamed timbers were of white oak, the

136

planking Georgia pine, and the deck yellow pine. Spruce was used for the masts and spars. The *Sirius* had no engine.

In building his copy, Carr made some slight alterations to the lines of the original. He wrote:

The sheer line I put down arbitrarily, though I don't think it differed much from Slocum's. When I set up the moulds and ran the sheer ribband I made some slight changes as is usual in such cases. Lines sometimes appear differently when they are on the floor in two dimensions from what they appear in the boat when they have three. I purposely flattened out the buttocks of the boat perhaps an inch or so as I thought they showed a little drag in the book. The change was of little consequence, I believe. Also I did change the appearance of the stern a little above the waterline thinking to beautify it. The *Spray*, I thought, looked just a little boxy with the square corners of her stern bulwarks and the face of the transom not protruding above the deck line and I tried to overcome that.

The *Sirius* was launched at Shelburne Harbor, Vermont, and after being rigged and fitted out, left Montreal in October 1957, and sailed down the St. Lawrence River to the sea. Carr had a companion aboard as far as Nova Scotia, where he spent the winter completing the fitting out. He then sailed down to Hampton, Virginia, and Charleston, South Carolina, before returning north to Nova Scotia. Both those trips were made alone.

THE *Success II*

A *Spray* hull was recently built at Cowes, Isle of Wight, by David Cheverton and Partners, for a retired Army officer, Captain J. J. Cappelen, Jr., of Williamsburg, Virginia. Construction was started in April 1958. The vessel had an English oak keel, laminated mahogany stem, oak steamed timbers, and 1-inch African mahogany planking. The oak used was cut from the Parkhurst Forest. The hull, without deck, was completed by January 1959, and shipped to Williamsburg, where the owner is at present finishing the construction himself. He is planning a

137

round-the-world voyage, and has sheathed the hull with ⅛-inch fiberglas as a protection against marine borers. An Enfield Diesel engine is to be fitted as auxiliary.

Captain Cappelen wrote:

My wife and I were stationed in Europe and were aware that the Dutch, Belgians, and Germans are building new boats, sending them to the United States, and underselling the American market. We found their price too high, however, and thus started looking for used boats in the British yachting magazines. After a thorough search, we found that although there were some excellent buys, no used boat had all the features we wanted. We are going to retire in three years in the Virgin Islands and want a good, sound, solid cruising boat with shoal draft. After searching many designs, we came onto the *Spray*; she is just what we want. I would not change an inch of her hull or underbody, but I am putting on a modern house and a Marconi rig.

I utilized the lines in Slocum's book, blew them up photographically, and made a body plan, half-breadth plan and sheer plan in proper scale. This is what Cheverton and Partners are lofting from.

THE *Sojourner*

The most recent copy of the *Spray* to be built was owned by another United States Army officer, Captain Andrew G. Brunn, of New York. This is a slightly enlarged version, having an additional frame in the midship section to make the vessel 44 feet in length. She was built from Victor Slocum's plans by the veteran shipwright John E. Gamage of Rockland, Maine. The *Maine Coast Fisherman* carried a report on the building of the *Sojourner*:

John E. Gamage of this seacoast town has probably built more wooden ship tonnage than any man living today (well over 100,000 tons, by his own estimate), but the chances are that the 44-foot vessel now being framed at the Snow Boat Yard here will bring this master builder more satisfaction, foot for foot, than anything he's tackled in his long career. Sixty-five years ago, when Captain Joshua Slocum made his famous solo sailing trip around the world

138

he started something. More accurately, his little wooden vessel did. When the captain stated in his book "Sailing Alone Around the World" that, in the course of a 23-day 2,700-mile journey, he found it necessary to stay at the wheel but one hour, it was inevitable that sailing men all over the globe would look to the lines of his yawl, *Spray*. That is, if what they wanted was a seaworthy little craft that needed little tending. . . .

"I'd quit the boatbuilding trade. I was selling insurance when this fellow got in touch with me," John Gamage reports. "He wanted a copy of the *Spray*, and he figured I was the man who could build her the way he wanted her built. He was planning to retire from the army, and he and his wife were going to sail around the world; so he wanted a vessel built in the old-fashioned way, solid, strong, and with no skimping on time and materials." [23]

There appears to have been little skimping on money either, and this copy of the *Spray* would undoubtedly be the most expensive ever constructed. The total cost was originally estimated at $45,000, but the figure was subsequently said to be about double this.

The keel and frames are of gray oak—the nearest American equivalent to English oak—and the planking is native cedar. Some of the scantlings are: keel, stem, sternpost, all 8-inch sided, garboard 2½ inches, planking 2 inches, shelf and clamps, 3 by 6 inches, frame, 3 by 4 inches, deck beams 4 by 6 inches. All fastenings are Everdur or Monel. An unusual feature is a watertight "collision" bulkhead between forepeak and cabin. The ballast is all inside, 7 to 8 tons of pig lead, and auxiliary power is provided by a 71-horsepower General Motors Diesel engine. Captain Brunn intended to rig the vessel as a gaff ketch and to make it his home on retirement. Fate, however, played a heavy hand in this dream; Brunn died of leukemia in New York in 1964. The vessel was purchased in 1963 by Richard Nakashian, who completed the fitting out, renamed her the *Spray*, and for the last two years has been running charter parties around Boston Harbor, Massachusetts. The *Spray* is licensed to carry a total of 49 passengers and a crew of four.

THE LAKE VICTORIA *Spray*

A unique copy was built on the shores of Lake Victoria, East Africa, by Henry C. Longmore, from 1953 to 1955. This little boat is only 19 feet long, and is probably the smallest copy of the *Spray* ever built. Mr. Longmore wrote:

I blew up the plans from a Penguin edition of Slocum's book, and as you can see from the photographs, made several modifications. Starting with the keel, I extended the depth by 6 inches (on my half scale) and this was done by bolting a 6-by-3-inch steel H-section beam to the woodwork and flaring the stem into this. The sides of the beam were filled with concrete, but I doubt if together they weighed more than 300 pounds.

The hull itself was as near as possible to Slocum's, and the rigging was a sloop, similar to the original *Spray*'s first rig. I took rather a liberty with my half size job and called it *Spray*. I hope Jos. Slocum didn't mind. . . .

The next owner of the little vessel, William John Mullis, of Kampala, Uganda, said:

Mr. Longmore intended to rail her to Mombasa and sail her down to Durban, but instead of Durban he had to go to Bulawayo, before he had a chance to sail her much. She lay on moorings on the lake and gradually deteriorated for over two years. Several of Longmore's friends borrowed her and sailed her at times, but no maintenance took place, and gradually these people either lost interest in sailing, were posted home or to other places. She just lay at anchor neglected by everyone and finally the club committee decided that something would have to be done to clear the horrible looking thing away from the club moorings. So I had a look at her, found the whole of the cockpit had dry rot, the boom had dry rot, and all the running rigging was rotten, but the frames, keel, and planks were sound. I made Longmore an offer and he accepted. Since then I have been busily engaged in refitting her.

She is exactly half full size—19 feet O.A., and has gaff mainsail and jib, or rather she is rigged for that, as the sails don't exist any more. I am expecting some from England very shortly. She has mahogany frames and planking, and a mahogany deck and cabin trunk. There is sitting room only in the cabin, with two bunks. Of course she looks old fashioned by today's standards, but is a real boat in all respects.

THE BANGKOK *Spray*

In his book *Macpherson's Voyages*, A. G. H. Macpherson mentions meeting a copy of the *Spray* in Dobo, in the Spice Islands, in January 1938. "A most interesting vessel . . . the supply cutter *Spray*, built at Bangkok by a Swiss from the blueprints of Captain Slocum's famous little packet. . . ." [24]

Macpherson's sailing companion, William Leng, wrote: "I was with Mr. Macpherson when we looked over the supply cutter in Dobo; they told us the Swiss had her built from the plans in the book 'Sailing Alone Around the World' by Capt. Slocum." Leng added that the *Spray* was then owned by the Celebes Trading Company.

BEHAVIOR

BALANCE

One of the most remarkable things about the *Spray*, and that for which she is best remembered, was her ability to sail herself before the wind under ordinary canvas for days and weeks at a time. The average yacht might hold her course unattended for a time on the wind, but if she is to be made to steer herself with the wind aft, she will need special running sails. On a downwind course, the fore and aft rig is, theoretically unbalanced, because the sails are set to leeward of the hull producing a luffing moment. In practice, however, some ocean cruisers have steered themselves under working canvas off the wind—Admiral Goldsmith's *Rame* was one—but such boats are very rare indeed. There is no doubt that the ability to sail unattended is especially valuable for the cruising vessel; in the case of the singlehanded sailor, it is probably the most valuable attribute his boat could possess.

Since the advent of the twin foresail rig, pioneered by Ot-

142

way Waller in 1930, and now used widely by small boat sailors on long voyages, ocean cruising has become more enjoyable. With this system, even the worst-balanced boat can be left to itself on a trade wind run, thus relieving the crew of what has been aptly termed the "tyranny of the helm." There is time to work about the ship, doing all the little jobs that need to be done on any ocean passage, as well as time to eat, rest and sleep. The *Spray* had no special running sails, but with the perfect balance inherent in her hull, hardly needed any. It may not be entirely a coincidence that the docile steering qualities of the *Spray* were also to be found in other American coasters, particularly the oyster smacks, whose crews would have quite enough to do handling gear without wasting time at the helm. Such difficulties would no doubt have influenced the empirical development of these vessels long before similar problems arose with yachts.

The unique self-steering ability which the *Spray* showed throughout her long voyage became apparent to Captain Slocum shortly after setting out. However, it is likely that he was already aware of it before this. While Slocum was making final preparations for the world trip, reporters from the local newspapers paid him a visit. In response to queries as to how he would handle the boat by himself and get adequate rest, he said: "Understanding nautical astronomy, I will, of course, navigate the world around with some degree of precision natural to any first-rate navigator. But there is one thing new in my outfit, already tested, the workings of which you will hear of in my letters. . . . It will be of great value at sea. . . . Without it I could hardly dare to go on a voyage alone." [1]

In another paper of the same date, the report was more enlightening. Slocum said: "I have a steering gear which will act automatically when the boat is once laid on her course, and that will give me some chance to rest." [2]

Had Slocum a "steering gear," or was this merely the *Spray*'s wonderful balance itself—embraced by a term the average person could understand? Indeed, who would have believed him if he said that the *Spray* steered herself, and there would be no need to be on deck all the time? Before leaving America, Slocum

143

spent a season fishing on the coast, getting to know his boat, and it would be strange indeed if such an experienced mariner as he had not found some evidence of her self-steering ability during that time.

In any case, it soon showed out after leaving. Four days out from Sable Island, with the wind dead aft. ". . . the *Spray*, after having steered all day over a lumpy sea, took it into her head to go without the helmsman's aid . . . heading southeast, and making about eight knots, her very best work." In the next few days, the wind rose to a gale and the seas increased. "The waves rose high, but I had a good ship. . . . I lashed the helm, and my vessel held her course, and while she sailed I slept." [3]

The second week out, the *Spray* was again on her own. "My ship was sailing along now without attention to the helm. The wind was south; she was heading east. Her sails were trimmed like the sails of the nautilus. They drew steadily all night. I went frequently on deck, but found all well." [4]

After leaving the Azores, Slocum unwisely mixed the cheese and plums he had been given ashore, and was doubled up with cramps. The wind was increasing, and there were signs of a coming gale. "I should have laid to, but did not. I gave her the double-reefed mainsail and whole jib instead, and set her on her course." Slocum was delirious throughout the night and imagined that one of Columbus's crew, the pilot of the *Pinta*, was guiding his little ship on her course. In the morning he had recovered. "To my astonishment, I saw now at broad day that the *Spray* was still heading as I had left her, and was going like a race-horse. Columbus himself could not have held her more exactly on her course. The sloop had made ninety miles in the night through a rough sea." [5]

By the time the captain crossed the Atlantic, he knew that he had a self-steering ship. Outward bound from Gibraltar in the steady northeast trades, the *Spray* looked after herself: "The *Spray* had now settled down to the trade-winds and to the business of her voyage. . . . My ship, running now in the full swing of the trades, left me days to myself for rest and recuperation. I employed the time in reading and writing, or in whatever I found to do about the rigging and the sails to keep them all in order." [6]

The *Spray* really showed what she could do on the passage from Juan Fernandez to the Marquesas. The trades were strong and she flew along with a bone in her teeth:

I sailed with a free wind day after day . . . for one whole month my vessel held her course true; I had not, the while, so much as a light in the binnacle . . . I awoke, sometimes, to find the sun already shining into my cabin. I heard water rushing by, with only a thin plank between me and the depths, and I said, "How is this?" But it was all right; it was my ship on her course, sailing as no other ship has ever sailed before in the world. The rushing water along her side told me that she was sailing at full speed. I knew that no human hand was at the helm.[7]

And, after forty-three days, the landfall was true—the first of the Marquesas came into view ahead.

Even Slocum himself, who had become accustomed to the unique traits of the *Spray*, was astonished by her performance on the run from Thursday Island to the Cocos Islands. This was by far the supreme achievement of the voyage as far as self-steering was concerned, and made a profound impression on the old captain. The atoll was small and could easily be missed entirely, thus it was necessary to keep a very true course. After a passage of twenty-three days, the island was made out, dead ahead:

I saw from half-way up the mast cocoanut-trees standing out of the water ahead. I expected to see this; still it thrilled me as an electric shock might have done. I slid down the mast, trembling under the strangest sensations; and not able to resist the impulse, I sat on deck and gave way to my emotions. To folks in a parlor on shore this may seem weak indeed, but I am telling the story of a voyage alone.

I didn't touch the helm, for with the current and the heave of the sea the sloop found herself at the end of the run absolutely in the fairway of the channel. You couldn't have beaten it in the navy! Then I trimmed her sails by the wind, took the helm, and flogged her up the couple of miles or so abreast the harbor landing where I cast anchor at 3.30 p.m., July 17, 1897, twenty-three days from Thursday Island. The distance was twenty-seven hundred miles as the crow flies. This would have been a fair Atlantic voyage. It was a delightful sail! During those twenty-three days I had not spent altogether more than three hours at the helm, including the time occupied in beating into Keeling harbor. I just lashed the helm and let her go; whether the wind was abeam or dead aft, it was all the same: she always sailed on her course. No part of the voyage up to this point, taking it by and large, had been so finished as this.[8]

Running the southeast trades from Cape Town to St. Helena, the *Spray*, as usual, sailed herself: "I dipped into the new books given me at the cape, reading day and night. March 30 was for me a fast-day in honor of them. I read on, oblivious of hunger or wind or sea. . . ." When the island rose up out of the sea, right ahead, "I reached for a bottle of wine out of the locker, and took a long pull from it to the health of my invisible helmsman—the pilot of the *Pinta*." [9]

In the Appendix to his book, Slocum summed up the balance of the *Spray:* "With her boom broad off and with the wind two points on the quarter the *Spray* sailed her truest course. It never took too long to find the amount of helm, or angle of rudder, required to hold her on her course, and when that was found I lashed the wheel with it at that angle. The mainsail then drove her, and the main-jib, with its sheet boused flat amidships or a little to one side or the other, added greatly to the steadying power. . . . She was easily balanced and easily kept in trim." [10]

With an increasing wind, a yacht's balance tends to become worse. Slocum countered the extra weather helm in a hard wind with his flying jib: "Then if the wind was even strong or squally I would sometimes set a flying-jib also, on a pole rigged out on the bowsprit, with the sheets hauled flat amidships, which was a safe thing to do, even in a gale of wind." [11] This acted like a weather vane out in front of the boat, and apparently restored the balance by holding her stern to the wind against the luffing moment of the mainsail.

Since the great majority of small boats are unable to sail themselves for even a short time under normal fore-and-aft canvas, it was perhaps only natural that many people, including capable sailors, doubted Slocum's assertions as to the extraordinary ability of his *Spray*. That this vessel could steer herself for weeks on end, while he remained below cooking, reading, mending his sails, or sleeping, seems quite fantastic. A columnist of *The New York Times* aired the doubts of many who thought that Slocum's story of the *Spray* sailing herself was only a fairy tale. "Capt. Slocum repeatedly asserts that the *Spray* was so rigged that she both could and would steer herself, or to paraphrase his statements more explicitly that he could so arrange his sails and so lash his rudder that his boat would keep on her course all night. . . . The tale is painfully hard to believe." [12]

Slocum's reply was published in the newspaper four days later. He said that he regretted not having had the opportunity of taking his critics for a sail in the *Spray* to demonstrate her prowess. He commented further in his book:

Having had no yachting experience at all, I had no means of knowing that the trim vessels seen in our harbors and near the land could not all do as much, or even more, than the *Spray*, sailing, for example, on a course with the helm lashed.

I was aware that no other vessel had sailed in this manner around the globe, but would have been loath to say that another could not do it, or that many men had not sailed vessels of a certain rig in that manner as far as they wished to go. I was greatly amused, therefore, by the flat assertions of an expert that it could not be done . . . Some of the oldest and ablest shipmasters have asked how it was possible for her to hold a true course before the wind, which was just what the *Spray* did for weeks together. One of these gentlemen, a highly esteemed shipmaster, testified as government expert in a famous murder trial in Boston, not long since, that a ship would not hold her course long enough for the steersman to leave the helm to cut the captain's throat. Ordinarily it would be so. One might say that with a square-rigged ship it would always be so. But the *Spray*, at the moment of the tragedy in question, was sailing around the globe with no one at the helm, except at intervals more or less rare.[13]

147

Despite Slocum's assertions, there are many yachtsmen who still belive that he vastly exaggerated. However, the archives of numerous provincial newspapers all around the world contain testimony of his arrival and departure times, and these were corroborated in each case by the personal curiosity of hundreds of sightseers. There is thus no ground for questioning the authenticity of his passage times, yet some yachtsmen still fail to see that these would have been physically impossible for any man sailing alone if he had not been able to leave the helm for rest and sleep. That in itself is sufficient proof of the *Spray*'s qualities.

In *Yachting Monthly* many years ago, there was some interesting correspondence about a proposed designing competition for an ideal round-the-world cruiser. As the *Spray* was mentioned, this was referred to as the "Slocum Class" cruiser. The discussion touched on the *Spray*'s ability to sail herself, and is a good illustration of the attitude of many people, past and present, to this unique feature of the old vessel.

"A Cruiser" set the ball rolling:

Sir—May I suggest a designing competition for the best small boat to do a trip round the world in? I have heard several men in this service say that is what they will do when the war is over, and there must be many soldiers of the same mind. I am sure many of your designers could turn out a prettier, faster, and more yachty little vessel than Captain Slocum's *Spray*, yet equally seaworthy.[14]

The idea was supported by "Nab" in the next issue:

Sir—Please allow me to back "A Cruiser's" suggestion for a competition for the best small boat to go round the world in. It is an inspiration.

And the conception of our well known designers of ordinary small cruisers would be most interesting.

Personally, I cannot conceive any vessel rigged fore-and-after running true on her course hour after hour with no one at the helm. Yet both Capt. Slocum with his *Spray* and Jack London with his *Snark*, have accomplished it. *Spray* was the bottom of an old hulk "rose-on" (as the faculty says) by the owner. A most unpromising combination.[15]

The *Spray*

"As for myself the wonderful sea charmed me from the first"
Joshua Slocum

1. The *Spray* in Sydney Harbor, Australia. (Photo autographed by Joshua Slocum.)

2. The *Spray* in Pernambuco, Brazil, in 1895. (Reproduced in *The Voyages of Joshua Slocum* by Walter Magnes Teller; original photo courtesy of B. A. Slocum.)

3. The *Spray* at Shell Cove, Sydney Harbor, in 1896. (Author's photo; reproduced in *The Voyages of Joshua Slocum* by Walter Magnes Teller.)

4. The *Spray* hauled out at Devonport, Tasmania, in March 1897. (Photo by W. Aikenhead; reproduced in *The Search for Captain Slocum* by Walter Magnes Teller.)

5. The *Spray* in Providence Harbor, Rhode Island, in 1906. (Photo by E. P. McLaughlin; reproduced in *The Life and Voyages of Captain Joshua Slocum* by Victor Slocum.)

6. Nineteenth-century oyster-fishing sloops off Bridgeport, Connecticut; note similarity to the *Spray*. (Photo courtesy of the Smithsonian Institution.)

8. The *Spray* under sail in Branford Harbor, Connecticut, in about 1908. (Photo by N. B. Brainard; reproduced in *The Search for Captain Slocum* by Walter Magnes Teller.)

7. The *Spray* sailing herself. (Reproduced from *Rudder* magazine.)

9. The *Spray* at Washington, D. C., in May 1907. (Photo courtesy of A. L. Budlong.)

10. The *Spray* in Cotuit Harbor, Massachusetts, in the summer of 1909; the last known photograph of the vessel. (Photo courtesy of W. A. Nickerson.)

11. Dust Jacket of *Capt. Joshua Slocum* by Victor Slocum, depicting the *Spray* under full sail. The hand-printed inscription is by Benjamin Aymar Slocum. (Author's collection.)

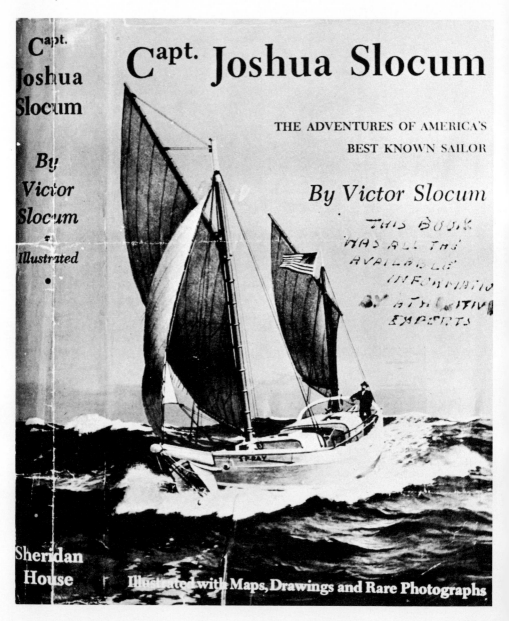

12. The *Ulula* sailing in the Bristol Channel, United Kingdom. (Photo courtesy of Charles Hinman.)

13. The St. Kilda *Spray*, refitted and relaunched, under sail on Port Phillip Bay, Melbourne, in 1963. (Photo courtesy of Jack Read.)

14. The *Pandora* in New York Harbor in 1911, on her ill-fated round-the-world cruise. (Photo courtesy of Richard Gordon McCloskey.)

15. The Oxford *Spray*, built by Robert D. Culler in 1929 at Oxford, Maryland. (Photo courtesy of Mystic Seaport, Mystic, Connecticut.)

16. The *Basilisk*, built in 1930 by Gilbert Klingel, hauled out at Oxford, Maryland. (Reproduced from *Natural History* magazine.)
    a. (*Above*) The bow
    b. (*Above right*) The stern

17. The cabin of the *Basilisk*. (Reproduced from *Natural History* magazine.)
    a. The laboratory workbench
    b. The living quarters, with two bunks

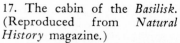

18. The *Igdrasil* under sail in the lagoon of the Cocos Islands. (Photo courtesy of Roger S. Strout.)

19. The cabin of the *Igdrasil*. (Photo courtesy of Roger S. Strout.)

20. The *Shamrock* in Port Phillip Bay, Melbourne. (Photo courtesy of A. Stanley Dickson.)

21. The *Sirius* at Hampton, Virginia, in 1959. (Photo courtesy of Capt. J. J. Cappelen, Jr.)

22. The *Foam*, a schooner-rigged copy of the *Spray*, under sail in 1930. (Photo courtesy of Horace W. Schmahl.)

23. (*Right*) The *Sojourner*, now renamed the *Spray*, under sail in Boston Harbor, Massachusetts, in 1965. (Photo courtesy of Richard Nakashian.)

24. (*Left*) The *Sol-Lys* in Dover Harbor, United Kingdom, in 1958. (Photo courtesy of John Mannering.)

25. Scale model of the *Spray* built by Benjamin Aymar Slocum, in the Peabody Museum, Salem, Massachusetts. (Photo courtesy of the Peabody Museum.)

The following month "Machine Gunner" was skeptical of the value of such a competition:

Sir—Far be it from me to throw cold water on the suggestion for a designing competition for a small ocean cruiser class, but what qualities do "A Cruiser" and "Nab" look for in such craft over and above those of an ideal cruiser?

I do not see that there can be any productive of a distinct type. There would, of course, have to be ample space allotted to stores and water tanks; scantlings would be heavy, and sail area small. That is all one would expect in such a vessel.

If the object is to produce a hull form and rig that would have the invaluable power of running free unattended, a designing competition would have little value. Such a vessel could only be evolved by long and costly practical experiment, if at all. With our present lack of knowledge no one could, from a mere scrutiny of the design and sail plan, definitely credit a particular boat with this quality.

My own experiments in this direction have met with very limited success. In light weather I have induced a two-masted lugger to run unsteered for about an hour by squaring off the goose-winged booms to the fullest extent permitted by the shrouds.

But after considerable experience with small craft at sea, and many experiments, I do not believe, and never shall till I see it, that any small vessel will run unattended before a smart breeze and following sea.[16]

Corresponding in the next issue, Elliot Giles pointed out the danger of self-steering with no-one on watch:

Sir—I have been greatly interested in the proposal to have a designing competition for a small ocean-going cruiser class, and wish most heartily to support such a project. But before we actually set to work I think we ought to try to agree about the essential points that we look for in an ocean-going cruiser. Your correspondent "Machine Gunner" is, I think, not far from the mark in his idea that she would simply be our ideal cruiser, with possibly extra room for water and stores. Since, however, Captain Slocum's name has been mentioned in connection with the subject, there appears to be a kind of implication that our cruiser should possess *Spray*'s unique faculty of sailing herself. Without entering at all into the possibility or otherwise of a small vessel's running free for days on end with the helm lashed, I wish to protest very strongly against harboring any such idea for our little ship. In the first place, probably very few of us have the experience and skill that Slocum had; and, even if we had it, the fact that he succeeded in sailing round the world is not any reason why we should copy his methods of navigation. For it remains true that sailing the ocean in a small vessel is a safe occupation only so long as one keeps an incessant look-out. So, even if a boat can sail unattended and unwatched, she should never be allowed to do so for any length of time. Our ideal cruiser would certainly be able to look after herself for a few hours, when sailing to some extent on a wind, and she might be asked to do that for stretches in fine, settled weather when no other vessel was in sight, but it is all that she ought to be asked to do.[17]

The amateur designer T. Harrison Butler then entered the discussion. He also refused to accept Slocum's statements:

Sir—I think that a yacht which is designed for the sort of work performed by Captain Slocum should be a very different craft from the *Spray*. I have always taken much of what is written in his "Voyage" as due to the literary abilities of the journalist who wrote it. Captain Slocum certainly sailed round the world, but sundry embellishments were necessary to make the book readable by the general public. I shall never be able to believe that any fore-and-aft-rigged vessel could sail before the wind for any length of time. The sail being all on one side tends to bring the boat to the wind; this tendency is corrected by helm. If the wind were absolutely constant and the sea smooth, the boat might keep a corrected course; but these conditions cannot be realized. Even with head-sails alone, most boats tend to come on to a reach. My *Sandhook* with both head-sails set and free helm sails herself on a reach, and shows no tendency to run or even to reach broad. I once had a small model with a very flat floor and hard bilges. I fitted a long fin keel. This boat would run dead with a square sail and jib sheeted flat. A well-designed yacht might do this, and even if she came up at times, she would make a general course to leeward. But with the mainsail set it seems to me to be frankly impossible, and in the case of a beamy shallow craft like the *Spray* it is incredible.[18]

In a later issue, E. Riddehough not only questioned the *Spray*'s running ability, but disputed the fact that she ran at all:

Sir—Don't you think that one or two of your correspondents are incorrect in assuming that Captain Slocum "ran" his boat for days without being at the helm? I have read his book, and I understood that he was "reaching" in the trades. No one could "run" a fore-and-after (unless perhaps a schooner goosewinged) without being at the wheel.[19]

Mr. Riddehough should have read the book more carefully. There were many occasions when the *Spray* steered herself for long periods with the wind dead aft, for example, three weeks in the northeast trades from the Canary Islands to the Equator, and forty-three days in the Southeast trades from Juan Fernandez to the Marquesas.

In the same issue, the editor, signing himself "M.I.N.A.," rounded up the discussion:

I am indebted to a correspondent for some interesting notes on Captain Slocum, published in an American paper in the early summer of 1908. It was on his return from what he termed a bagatelle of a cruise which he made in order to spend the winter in the West Indies. Here again he refers to the self-steering qualities of his boat which have aroused so much curiosity on the part of our readers. In answer to an inquiry as to how he cooked, slept, and ate, he said: "Same way I did on my other voyage—tie her helm up, balance my sails against the wind and let her go. Many and many a night have I slept peacefully and quietly, while the old girl sailed herself, and sailed as true and as quiet as a ship of ten thousand tons." [20]

Apart from the facts of Slocum's ocean passages, his own statements about the *Spray*'s balance are substantiated by the evidence of other people who witnessed her remarkable behavior.

On the trip up the River Plate from Montevideo to Buenos Aires, Slocum had on board an old friend from Cape Cod, Captain Howard. The *Spray* sailed

with a gale of wind and a current so much in her favor that she outdid herself. I was glad to have a sailor of Howard's experience on board to witness her performance of sailing with no living being at the helm. Howard sat near the binnacle and watched the compass while the sloop held her course so steadily that one would have declared that the card was nailed fast. Not a quarter of a point did she deviate from her course. My old friend had owned and sailed a pilot-sloop on the river for many years, but this feat took the wind out of his sails at last, and he cried, "I'll be stranded on Chico Bank if ever I saw the like of it!" Perhaps he had never given his sloop a chance to show what she could do. The point I make for the *Spray* here, above all other points, is that she sailed in shoal water and in a strong current, with other difficult and unusual conditions. Captain Howard took all this into account.[21]

While the *Spray* made her own way through the darkness on the river, the two men swapped yarns:

Howard told me stories about the Fuegian cannibals as she reeled along, and I told him about the pilot of the *Pinta* steering my vessel through the storm off the coast of the Azores, and that I looked for him at the helm in a gale such as this. I do not charge Howard with superstition,—we are none of us superstitious, —but when I spoke about his returning to Montevideo on the *Spray* he shook his head and took a steam-packet instead.[22]

Archibald B. Roosevelt, son of Theodore Roosevelt, became very friendly with Slocum and spent a week sailing with him on the *Spray*. He wrote in a letter:

You must realize that my cruise with Captain Slocum took place many years ago and I was a small boy at the time. Therefore I am relying on my memory over many years. You ask about self-steering. I can pretty definitely state that both on and off the wind in steady breezes, the *Spray* gave a remarkable exhibition of holding a course. I could not say that she would run that way indefinitely but, so far as I know, unless the wind changed or freshened or something of that sort, she continued to keep a pretty steady course.

Harold S. Smith, at the time a young yachtsman, went aboard the *Spray* with some friends in 1908 at Fairhaven, Massachusetts, and Slocum took them for a sail down Buzzards Bay. He said:

We were all allowed a trick at the wheel, and I was amazed at the old tub's easy steering . . . once sheets had been properly trimmed, she would steer herself for an indefinite time, to such an extent that a trick at the wheel was rather monotonous and somewhat unnecessary.[23]

Smith added in a letter, "The *Spray* steered almost perfectly with the wheel lashed with the wind in any direction from forward that would fill her sails to right astern."

In his book "Temptress Returns," Edward Allcard wrote: "There was a replica of the *Spray* built, but strangely enough, this boat did not have the same remarkable characteristics—maybe because she did not have the same remarkable Captain." [24]

Captain R. D. (Pete) Culler, original owner and builder of the Oxford *Spray*, said:

I'm sure the *Spray* model referred to was mine; he [Allcard] went skipper on her for a summer after I sold her. Now, with his experience, if he couldn't make her steer for him, there is something mighty wrong. She tended to do it herself anyway. For me, she always was a good self-steerer—the best—and I don't think the new owner loading her with electronic trash and having her all out of trim made too much difference. I went skipper on her for a summer for him and she still self-steered though she was sluggish. Of course later on they put a mechanical self-steering machine on her and I hear it would never work. Owner couldn't stand the sight of her old stub tiller, tackles, blocks and drum, which used to creak knowingly to itself as she went about her business of steering herself. I think the whole trouble is, that when they chucked the old gear over the side and went mechanical, they chucked their brains with it and didn't realize it. Or you can look at it another way. At the time they turned the after deck into a machine shop, the Pilot of the *Pinta* went over the side too, looking for another berth with oak and hemp instead of kilowatts.

In her article on the Oxford *Spray* in *Rudder*, Mrs. Toni Culler wrote: "She's all Slocum said she was as to steering herself. Many a time I have come up on deck to find the wheel lashed and Pete up in the bow washing down, taking

153

pictures or just taking it easy. This is apt to be disconcerting, especially when running down a dredged cut. Pete, however, insists that the old girl has run the Inland Waterway enough now to know her own way. And I believe she does!" [25]

Captain Culler added in a letter:

As to steering, she would do it herself on all points, so long as the wind was steady. This was more important than a regular sea. Naturally, in an unsteady wind she would tend to follow the wind; also varied strength would upset things too. However, it was not the shaky business that goes on in the modern type of boat, but rather slower, so you had some time to do something about it. . . . It was usual for my wife to find me wandering around the deck or below during my watch, and she thought nothing of it. However, it sort of unnerved strangers to the vessel but these soon gained confidence; so you see it was normal procedure and others accepted it, though seldom understood it. Naturally we kept a good lookout when doing this sort of thing along shore or in traffic. It's a very pleasant way to sail as it gives the watch so much time to do things that usually fall to the watch below. Also, one gets less cramped by long hours when one can move about.

Such was the remarkable balance of Culler's vessel that she would even steer herself under power:

Our ship would steer quite well, requiring attention about every five to ten minutes, usually the latter. In a canal that was straight with even banks, she would follow the center as long as the ditch lasted, if it stayed calm. She could wander a little when first put on course, until she balanced the water pressure on each side, then settle down. I often would go forward and wash down the decks, much to the amazement of people along the banks.

K. B. Johnstone, owner of the St. Kilda *Spray* for twenty years, also reported that his copy was well balanced. "We had her out in many blows and she performed as stated in Slocum's book. She could be made to sail in almost any direction unattended; we used to go below and have our lunch and leave her to it."

In his book *Inagua*, Gilbert Klingel commented on the *Basilisk*'s balance:

Captain Joshua Slocum, in telling of his voyage around the world in the original *Spray*, had claimed that for hundreds of miles his little ship had steered herself as accurately as if there had been a man at the wheel. Provided, of course, that the wind remained in the same quarter. The feat was accomplished by trimming and adjusting sail and rudder so that there was a perfect balance fore and aft. This claim has been disputed many times, but without foundation. We owe our lives to this one feature. For that evening, exhausted and weary, chilled to the marrow, unable to remain longer on deck, yet afraid to let the ship scud before the wind, we adjusted sail and rudder as Slocum had described. And in all that wild melee of storm the grand little ship plunged sturdily along, straight as an arrow, for the center of the ocean.

All through that night she sailed with not a soul on deck, tossed and beaten by the worst winter storm of 1929–30. Miles away the great schooner *Purnell T. White*, in whose company we had put to sea, was also fighting the gale and waging a losing battle. And far and wide, north and south of us that night on the broad Atlantic, sturdy steamers were sending out S.O.S. calls or limping into port with smashed houses and twisted decks. On and on we pressed, plunging through the waves, bobbing to the top and sliding down the valleys, proof that the old sea captain had not lied. A gallant little ship, the *Basilisk*. There should be more like her.[26]

Klingel said in a letter:

The balance was perfect at all points of sailing. I have never observed that an increase or decrease in the wind, or changing sea conditions, made any appreciable difference. Once properly set on her course, if the wind held steady, the boat remained perfectly balanced. The *Spray* is the most perfectly balanced ship that I have ever been on. For days on end, I have gone about my business on board and let the boat go her own way. The compass would swing at most a point or two one way or another and average out exactly on course. . . . My old *Spray* was so perfectly balanced I could sail her under main alone, under mizzen and jib, or with all three with never a thought to the wheel. I once sailed her 400 miles on a downwind course, wind 40 m.p.h. dead astern, and very heavy seas, under three-reefed main and full jib sheeted flat, and she held the course better than I could do at the wheel. . . . I could never observe any appreciable difference with the mizzen up or down. In fact, I think that the mizzen could have been dispensed with, in many cases, and it would have made no difference whatsoever.

It is interesting to compare Klingel's remarks about the mizzen with those of Slocum, who added a jigger to the *Spray* in the Magellan Strait. "The yawl-rig then adopted was an improvement only in that it reduced the size of a rather heavy mainsail and slightly improved her steering qualities on the wind. When the wind was aft the jigger was not in use; invariably it was then furled." [27]

Captain Culler found his mizzen on the Oxford *Spray* useful both on and off the wind. "Yes, I found the mizzen a help on a wind, think it allowed the main to be trimmed more suitably while it took over the work of balance. I found that dead before the wind with the mizzen wung-out eased the helm and made her very steady."

Mrs. Culler wrote in *Rudder*: "The lug mizzen is amazingly efficient and easy to handle. It works with a single halliard and requires no attention while tacking. With the wind aft we frequently sail into an anchorage under mizzen alone. She lays to under mizzen and will even get under way with it alone." [28]

Bob Carr wrote of his *Sirius:* "The boat steers herself well either on the wind or before it. Often I can't get her to hold the exact course I want but a point or so doesn't make so much difference out at sea."

T. A. Dickson wrote in *Rudder* of his sail on the *Pandora*:

With the first of early dawn, Saturday July 25th, sounded the click-click of the winch, as we took in the slack of the anchor chain prior to making sail, then a little difficulty getting the dinghy aboard, but finally we had to lower mainsail and lift her with the peak halyards; this soon overcame the trouble. Now with the mainsail up again, make your staysail fast the port side, weight anchor and off she pays on the port tack; a short board until we clear the end of the pier, and away; when we were free of all obstructions and could put her on a course. The sheets were trimmed, the wheel tied up; Arapakis went below to write up yesterday's log and Blythe disappeared down the forescuttle to prepare breakfast.

I had full possession of the deck where, for the first time, I had a practical example of the wonderful balance possessed by *Pandora*.

Certainly, then she was close-hauled, but though later the wind freed a point or two, and we eased the sheets accordingly, no one was required at the wheel. As instances of this selfsteering, I will mention that during breakfast and dinner—by no means hurried meals—nobody was even on deck. This was all very strange to me, for never previously had I sailed on Port Phillip Bay without some one's continual attention at the tiller. Not being able to make the West Channel, we decided on the South one. During the afternoon the wind fell very light and darkness found us just off Dromana, where we dropped anchor for the night.

Sunday morning, in a fresh Northeasterly, we soon ran the 8 or 10 miles to Queenscliff; with a free sheet and no one at the wheel.[29]

Thomas Fleming Day interviewed the crew of the *Pandora* in New York, and reported in *Rudder* on her self-steering ability:

There were days when there was nothing to do but read, write, sleep, or enjoy the fine weather. Captain Arapakis stated that it was not necessary to remain at the wheel. The wheel was set at noon, when observations were taken, and it was lashed in the position wanted. At the taking of the next noon observations the direction was changed as thought necessary. The Captain stated that in the run from Ascension Island to New York the wheel was practically untouched. A condition which should make life on the ocean wave very agreeable.[30]

One very interesting fact about the *Spray*'s balance is that almost all vessels based on her lines have proven equally good at sailing themselves, even though many were greatly modified. This remarkable balance is essentially inherent in the hull; the model is not at all critical, and the sail plan even less so, and it is thus possible to make extensive changes without impairing the self-steering qualities. In his book *Cruising Yachts—Design and Performance*, the late T. Harrison Butler wrote: "The fact is that if the hull is unbalanced no disposition of sail will maintain a balance. If the hull is balanced the yacht will have a very wide tolerance, and the sails can be placed more or less as you wish." [31] This certainly appears

157

to have been true of the *Spray* and her copies. In his article on the *Foam* design, John Hanna said: "Of course the hull is the great thing. It would do very well with a schooner rig . . . or any other rig one's personal fancy might prefer." [32] As we have already seen, one copy was rigged as a schooner.

There is no doubt that the ketch rig is the most popular for ocean cruising, and many *Spray* copies have been so rigged. One of these was the *Igdrasil* which, like the *Spray*, started off as a sloop. In *Yachting*, Roger Strout wrote:

Igdrasil was first rigged as a sloop with a 30-foot main boom, while a single big headsail filled the fore triangle. I was new to sailing then and it seemed sound reasoning that I could make fewer mistakes with two sails than with the four I now carry. . . . There were other reasons for this rig, however. An excellent suit of sails was available from the wrecked *Basilisk* and I had a sneaking desire to check up on some of Captain Slocum's stories of long stretches with no one at the helm. A year and a half under this rig convinced me that the stories were well within the bounds of possibility. . . .[33]

Strout found proof of Slocum's claims on the 3000-mile trade-wind passage from the Galapagos to the Marquesas. He reported in *Yachting*: "The wind never rose to the rollicking force five that the pilot charts promised; even force four, which we wanted, was rare indeed. Whatever the breeze, *Igdrasil* sailed peacefully on day and night under full sail with the wind two or three points on the quarter and no one at the wheel with never a jibe. *Igdrasil* was living up to the *Spray*'s reputation. In fact 25 nights out of 30, both of us got a full night's sleep." [34]

Strout enlarged on the *Igdrasil*'s balance in a letter:

With constant wind and sea she would hold a course anywhere from hard on the wind to dead before it. . . . As a ketch, in the Gulf of Alaska, with the mainsail furled, the two headsails sheeted hard and the 160 sq. ft. mizzen broad off, she did a steady 140 miles a day before a Force 8 gale. . . . In Auckland, when we were making a new suit of sails, a friend asked us to go on a club cruise down the gulf. We accepted and Mr. Jamieson and his family sailed with us.

While the new main and staysail were bent, the jib was still being roped, so we were unbalanced forward. However, we aimed her for the desired destination with the boom broad off, lashed the wheel, and all hands sat down on the cabin top for lunch. We kept far from the wheel, so that the many keelers that dashed up to look us over would know that we would not be altering course, regardless of the rules of the road. The visitor must often do that, since yachts frequently approach from all directions at once. We had to finish the jib and bend it to beat back, but down wind in smooth water she ran perfectly without it.

The *Starbound* was another ketch-rigged copy. The owner, J. Kenneth Whitteker, said: "Not having steady trade winds here on the North Atlantic seaboard, I have had but one good opportunity to make a check of her self-steering qualities. With the wind abeam on the starboard side she held her course for about 280 miles, then a calm followed by an abrupt change in wind made helm attention necessary."

L. H. Roberts wrote of his *Chack Chack:* "You asked would *Chack Chack* sail alone as the *Spray* did. Yes, I have had a few hours sleep here in this Gulf, and often my afternoon tea. Many a man has opened his eyes real wide as he has sat with me having tea as we sailed with one hand at the wheel. Nor was the wheel made fast in any way. I could set the rudder in center, set sail, and then leave her for the long run across the Gulf. Of course with different tides she would get off somewhat; but I've had three hours sleep and was but little off course when I went to the wheel."

Like the *Chack Chack*, the Rochester *Spray* was a copy whose lines had been modified quite a good deal from the original, yet she also had a good balance, according to her owner, Herr Leisegang: "She sailed herself for hours on end without anyone touching the helm and did not get off course so long as the Baltic wind remained favorable."

In streamlining the *Spray* to produce his more yachty *Foam* design, John Hanna succeeded in keeping her steering qualities. In a letter written in 1944 to an Australian admirer of the *Foam*, he said: "All owners have been most enthusiastic about

159

the seaworthiness and sea-ease of this boat. Particularly, they say she is simply marvelous for steadiness and easy steering when running before a bad following sea—the most dangerous form of sailing. She also will hold her course with lashed helm for many hours at a time, self-correcting any deviation."

Horace W. Schmahl, the owner of the first *Foam* ever built, wrote: "The *Island Trader* definitely does live up to the reputation of the *Spray*. She sails herself perfectly with the wind astern. I have never found that an increase in the wind made any difference in her self-steering characteristics."

There is one *Foam*, however, which apparently does not steer herself off the wind. Neal Small, owner of the *Sagamore*, stated in a letter: "I have never been able to adjust things for selfsteering with the wind aft. I do not believe it can be done with *Sagamore*'s rig. I wouldn't dare leave the wheel dead before it—and on a run of any distance we rigged a boom tackle to the lee chainplates—just to keep things a bit more stabilized. I think that phenomenal downwind run of *Spray* must have been due partly to Slocum's own genius. Maybe the pilot of the *Pinta* helped out. *Sagamore* will steer herself closehauled or on a reach—but then most boats with ample underbody profile will."

The English copy, the *Ulula*, was another which gave trouble when running. According to Charles Hinman, "she would sail with her helm lashed if the wind was forward of the beam. With her postwar rig (ketch) she handled beautifully. Before the wind she had to be steered all the time, although with spinnaker up she was easy."

Henry Longmore commented on the balance of his half-size *Spray:* "The trouble with lake winds is their constant changing, but with a stretch of fairly steady wind she would sail without altering the wheel."

Regarding the question of weather helm, Slocum had this to say: "The amount of helm required varied according to the amount of wind and its direction. These points are quickly gathered from practice. Briefly I have to say that when close-hauled in a light wind under all sail she required little or no weather helm. As the wind increased I would go on deck, if below, and turn the wheel up a spoke more or less, relash it, or, as the sailors say, put it in a becket, and then leave it as before." [35]

Under moderate conditions the *Spray* was very light on the helm, but there is naturally a limit to the amount of sail a hull even as well balanced as hers can carry with comfort in a strong blow. Shortly after setting out, the *Spray* was running from Boston to Gloucester to pick up some fisherman's stores. "The wind freshened, and the *Spray* rounded Deer Island light at the rate of seven knots. . . . The wind still freshening, I settled the throat of the mainsail to ease the sloop's helm, for I could hardly hold her before it with the whole mainsail set." [36]

After leaving Gibraltar, a furious gale sprang up and, to make matters worse, a Moorish pirate vessel gave chase. It was a race for life: "The *Spray* was doing nobly; she was even more than at her best; but, in spite of all I could do, she would broach now and then. She was carrying too much sail for safety." [37]

Strout reported of his *Igdrasil:* "In any full sail breeze she was well balanced. As the wind increased, either on the wind or running, more weather helm was required. Once, while dodging a cyclone in the Tasman Sea, I ran long stretches under staysail and triple-reefed main (5 ft. in each reef). The wind was so strong that even under this small canvas my wife was utterly unable to handle the wheel. I kept wheel watch for 13 hours straight and it was a fight every minute."

Charles Hinman, who had similar experience with his *Ulula,* wrote: "Before a fresh wind, say Force 6 to 7, she was a handful in a big sea." And he added: "The seas at the western end of the Bristol Channel are quite something."

The St. Kilda *Spray* was very light on the helm, according to her owner, K. B. Johnstone. "We could run before a stiff breeze or big seas and she would never take charge or race away; the wheel could be held in your fingers."

161

TO WINDWARD

In any discussion of the *Spray*, yachtsmen are quick to point out that she had mostly favorable winds on her passage around the world. "And, of course," they say, "even a haystack will go down wind." Doubtless this is true enough, but I imagine that some haystacks are better than others.

Attempting to belittle the *Spray*'s performance by sneering at running ability is hardly relevant, when almost all ocean work is done this way. Her track was projected in accordance with favorable winds and currents, as was the general practice of all sailing vessels up to her time. Common sense dictates no other course. Times change, however, and fashions with them, and the yachtsmen of today are more concerned with windward performance than qualities off the wind. The question everyone asks about the *Spray* is: "How is she on the wind?"

Harold S. Smith said of his short sail on the original *Spray*: "Under normal conditions *Spray* would easily sail within five points off the wind. However, she made considerable leeway when really close hauled. Six points off was probably her best wind for sailing."

In a letter in *Yachting Monthly*, Norman Deakin said of the Rochester *Spray*, "she was not a success in English waters, being very sluggish in her windward work."[38] Apparently German waters agreed with her better, as she performed well enough for Herr Leisegang. He wrote: "Because of the powerful, long, and deep keel the *Heimat* pointed high, tacking well at 4 points to the wind and making little leeway."

Horace W. Schmahl said: "The *Island Trader* does make quite a bit of leeway when close-hauled."

The St. Kilda *Spray* was also not good in this respect, according to K. B. Johnstone. "She made a lot of leeway without the engine running slowly."

Charles Hinman was happier with his copy. "*Ulula* had very little keel and her maximum draught was under six feet, so she made leeway when going to windward, as all boats will. The effect was minimized by her clean run which gave her a windward tendency which nearly compensated the natural leeway."

Neal Small stated that the *Sagamore* would point within 45 degrees of the wind, "no more for best speed—probably makes 10 degrees leeway."

The Lake Victoria *Spray* "would not point up very close to the wind, "wrote W. J. Mullis in a letter.

Bob Carr was more explicit about his *Sirius:* "How close she will sail depends on wind and sea. Ordinarily with a fresh breeze she should make good a course about six pts. from the direction of the wind."

Captain Culler found the same with his *Spray*. He said: "My vessel would lay five points from the wind in smooth water, but I found she did a little better making good about six points; this is similar to the coasters of my experience. In ordinary conditions she made about ¾-point leeway—I would say this was average with somewhat of a head sea and what I allowed in figuring a course. . . . *Spray* would not go to windward under jib alone though she would reach and tack under it in smooth water."

The *Igdrasil* also went fairly well in smooth water. Roger Strout commented: "With a pleasant breeze over the relatively smooth waters of Hauraki Gulf, she would point up surprisingly well. In fact, I once surprised the owner of a smart Auckland keeler by holding even with him for several miles while he was hard on the wind. . . . She would go nicely at five points under reasonable sea conditions. My sails were fully roped on the leach and so not adapted to close-winded work. You have to choose long sail life or snappy performance."

Gilbert Klingel had similar views. "*Basilisk* was not at her best closehauled. Under reasonable sea conditions she did not do much better than six points to the wind, but I did not feel that this was the fault of the hull in any way, but rather the heavy cruising canvas I was using. Ability to point is as much a matter of canvas as it is of hull form."

Furthermore, canvas is not the only other factor. Many

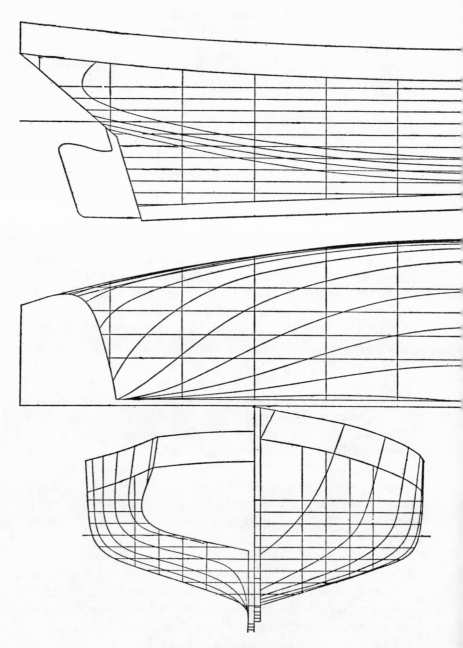

C. Lines of the *Spray*

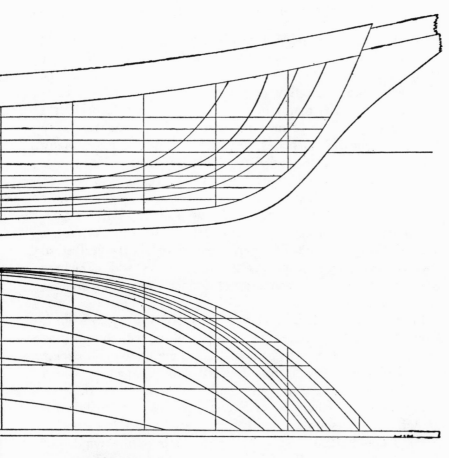

Length overall	41 feet	0 inches (including cutwater)
Length waterline	32 feet	1 inch
Beam extreme	14 feet	2 inches
Draft	4 feet	2 inches

Reproduced and drawn by Kenneth E. Slack, February 1962

165

yachtsmen tend to judge a boat's performance to windward
on hull form alone, especially the draft, but in fact many other
things are equally important. In his book *Ten Small Yachts*,
the well-known English designer Maurice Griffiths wrote:
"From many boats that I have sailed, and whose behaviour I
have studied, I have formed the opinion that a yacht's ability
to go to windward depends very little on her *draught*. Many
yachtsmen, and not a few yacht designers, imagine that unless
a yacht has a deep draught ('plenty of grip of the water')
she will be a poor performer to windward. If her waterlines
are too rounded, or her garboards too full, she will be slow
to windward in any case, whether she is a very deep or a
very shallow boat." [39] The performance of the typical shoal
and beamy American yachts in ocean races and elsewhere
rather gives the lie to some popular notions concerning draught
and weatherliness.

In his *Foam I* design, Hanna increased the *Spray*'s draft
from 4 feet to 5 feet. Five feet is still pretty conservative
by present-day standards, but on draft alone one would expect
a marked improvement in windward ability. *Foam II* had a
4-foot 6-inch draft and was similar in most other respects.
Hanna wrote of their comparative performance: "Sailing together there was no doubt that the second boat was better.
Foam I could point the merest trifle closer to the wind, but
Foam II, because of less frictional resistance, was a bit faster
on all points, and usually covered any given course in better
time." That six inches more draft increased the efficiency of
this design on the wind by "the merest trifle" would surely
show that draft is not the only factor to be considered.

Hanna's five-foot draft for the *Foam* was only one of his
concessions to fashion. He stated his own views in the article
on the design:

. . . deep draft is not necessary for running before the wind—and
both Davis and Atkin admit that ocean sailing must be practically
all off the wind—since the idea that small boats can get across the
ocean by fighting the wind, beating against it, is merely an idea in
the heads of smooth-water yachtsmen. *Spray* had sufficient draft to
sail well enough to windward to meet every emergency of 46,000

miles. . . . Her weakness to windward was not so much a matter of draft as of driving power for her heavy and blunt hull. Give her wind enough to drive her—and she was stiff enough to stand up and carry all the sail she needed when other boats were reefed—and she could step out to windward well enough to beat crack racing boats. There is no use saying she could not do this because there are plenty of men still living who saw her when she *did do it*.[40]

Under normal conditions, of course, the *Spray* was nowhere near as good on the wind as a modern yacht, and in the eyes of most yachtsmen, this damns her straightway. She would be of little use to the average boat owner who takes his craft out only on weekends for a short harbor trip. But for extended ocean work, the ability to point well, which is of such account in smooth water and coastal sailing, must take second place to the ability to carry sail. After his world passage in *Wanderer III*, Eric Hiscock said that six points off the wind was "as close as I believe it pays to sail in the open ocean." [41] Windward performance in ordinary weather and in heavy weather are two entirely different things. Extreme conditions of wind require a vessel which can stand up to her canvas; in this respect a tender craft is far less efficient by reason of her much decreased sail and keel area when heeled. After all, a boat is designed upright, and lying on one's beam ends is hardly a satisfactory or seamanlike way of reducing sail area. The normal yacht is certainly at a disadvantage here as she has to heel well over before her ballast keel can become effective. Because of tremendous stiffness, the *Spray* carries a lot of sail for a 37-foot boat, and can still carry it when the going gets tough—long after the average modern yacht has had to haul down to keep off her beam ends. This is what counts in an emergency. In his book *Cruising Under Sail*, Eric Hiscock wrote: "To sail on a long passage at a steep angle of heel is tiring for the ship's company and bad for their morale, and when clawing off a lee shore in a strong wind the safety of the yacht may depend on her ability to stand up to her canvas." [42]

Just after entering the Strait of Magellan, the *Spray* was struck by a terrific southwesterly gale, "like a shot from a cannon, and for the first half-hour it was something to be remembered by way of a gale. For thirty hours it kept on blowing hard. The sloop could carry no more than a three-reefed mainsail and forestaysail; with these she held on stoutly and was not blown out of the strait." [43]

After owning a *Spray* copy for twenty-three years, Captain Culler summed up the position. He said in a letter: "This windward performance is all relative. These modern things sail well on a wind in ordinary summer weather, yet I would put my faith in the *Spray* model. She would not make much or maybe gain any, but could hold her own on sheer ability to carry sail, which, in the classical tradition of the lee shore, is the most important—who can lug sail the longest."

STABILITY

With these preliminary comments on stiffness, we pass on now to the stability of the *Spray* in general.

Harold Smith said of the original: "She sailed at a very small angle of heel. . . ."

Captain Culler wrote of the Oxford *Spray*: "She was the best sail carrier of her size I've been in and her angle of heel the least I've ever seen. All coasters were pretty much the same and make the yacht type seem very tender."

Captain Clinton Baverstock commented on the *Sagamore:* "She is a very able boat and good sail carrier." Neal Small added that her stability was "excellent—with the wind about 30 knots the rail comes close to the water."

About the *Starbound*, Kenneth Whitteker said: "Sailing six points to the wind with a 30-m.p.h. breeze, she has about ten degrees of heel."

Roger Strout recalled in a letter: "At six knots close-hauled in smooth water *Igdrasil* heeled about two strakes (eleven inches) but I have had the rail, 16 inches above deck, go under in squalls."

Charles Hinman wrote of the *Ulula:* "Her great beam and about eight tons of ballast gave her great sail carrying power. We did not often have to reef her."

168

Horace W. Schmahl reported on his copy in detail:

The *Island Trader* is a very stable boat, despite the fact that her spars are solid and very heavy. With all her canvas up, that is, main-sail, topsail, foresail, working jib and flying jib, and at a 20-mile-an-hour breeze and close-hauled, she will heel at an angle of 12 to 15 degrees. On one occasion I took the vessel away from her berth in Greenport Harbor and out on the Sound in anticipation of a severe hurricane. I rode out the entire storm with bare poles without finding it overly uncomfortable. I might say that despite 120-mile gusts of wind, the *Island Trader* never listed more than five degrees except, of course, by reason of wave roll.

"Right," says the yachtsman, "so the *Spray* is very stiff initially, but what about ultimate stability? That's what really counts."

The *Spray* model is often criticized for shallow draft and lack of outside ballast and has been condemned by many people as unsafe for ocean work.

The relative merits of inside and outside ballast have been argued back and forth ever since the latter came into vogue. Eric Hiscock wrote: "Provided the inside ballast does not get adrift, the ballasted yacht will right herself." [44] John Hanna, in one of his regular articles in *Rudder*, made some scathing comments about the *Spray*, obviously directed at her all-inside ballast:

Since the Suicide Squad has been for many years building exact copies of *Spray*, and will continue doing so for many years more unless restrained, perhaps I can save a life or two by explaining as simply as possible, the basic reason (skipping many other good reasons) why *Spray* is the worst possible boat for anyone, and especially anyone lacking the experience and resourcefulness of Slocum, to take off soundings. It is for the same reason that the Cape Cod cat and the inland lake racing scow are not suitable for ocean going. Everyone who has handled these types knows that, though they are extremely stiff initially, if they are ever heeled beyond a critical point, they flop right over as inevitably as a soup plate, which they resemble. What a boat does in a coastal chop has no bearing on what it will do in the great waves of the deep sea. A big lurching cross sea, that would scarcely disturb a properly de-

169

signed hull, can—especially if it coincides, as it often does, with an extra-savage puff of a squall—flip over a *Spray* hull just as you would a poker chip. The capsizing of one *Spray* duplicate, off the coast of South America, was recorded in *Rudder* many years ago. Many duplicates trying to duplicate the circumnavigation have disappeared without trace, just as the original *Spray* and Slocum did. Others have been wrecked, with part or all of crew saved in various ways. Of the great fleet that has tried in all these years, but one *Spray* duplicate ever completed the circuit—Roger Strout's *Igdrasil*. And his published accounts of his voyage indicate that throughout the greater part of it he met generally favorable weather; also that he carried an immense fuel supply (in relation to the size of his engine) and ran every possible mile under power. Moreover, in letters to this writer, he has stated that on at least two occasions his vessel was flipped up to the very point of the last rollover, and for a second or two it seemed she would never come back on her bottom. After such experience, it is understandable that he says, if building again for such a trip, he would willingly sacrifice the much-loved comfort of broad decks and great initial stability for more of that *final* stability which infallibly rights a well-designed yacht even if knocked down with her masts in the water. I trust a little sober reflection on these facts will cause a ray of light to dawn in the minds of another generation of would-be *Spray* duplicators. The famous old ship had her good points, and no one admires them more than I; but not enough to overcome some almost certainly fatal faults.[45]

Surely these words would be enough to turn anyone off the *Spray* for good!

It is a pity that such a skilled architect and fine writer as John Hanna should have tried to substantiate his opinions with a lot of exaggerations and some definite falsehoods thrown up as facts. With all due respect to the late gentleman, who, in spite of this particular tirade, was one of the staunchest supporters of the *Spray* model, his forthright remarks are fallacious and, moreover, dishonest. Unfortunately, they cannot be excused on the grounds of ignorance, for he knew the facts better than most, and such distortion of the truth merely to make a point is hardly proper. For the sake of historical accuracy, and in all fairness to the old *Spray* herself, it is only right that the facts be presented.

The *Spray* duplicate referred to was the *Pandora*, which *did* capsize off the coast of South America—and also *did* right herself, a fact which Hanna conveniently neglected to mention. The story was told in *Rudder:*

On January 16, 1911, it is recounted in the log, *Pandora* passed Cape Horn. The wind was then blowing great guns, and the wind flung spray so high that it was impossible to see far ahead. The vessel passed within three and a half miles of shore in making the Cape. The object being to steer clear of any possible encounter with ice.

"We were near the Horn on January 22d," said Captain Arapakis, "when death nearly ended our voyage. A howling hurricane was kicking up an inferno of a sea, and the water was coming across our decks so fast that we appeared to be submerged. We carried no canvas and the wheel was lashed. Captain Blythe and myself were in the cabin and the hatch was battened down. Suddenly there came to us a sound like that of a hundred guns discharging, as a mighty wave thundered down squarely upon our deck.

"The vessel gave a list and then in a second she turned bottom up. The Captain and myself, with the instruments and everything in the cabin not made fast, went tumbling to the wall and then to the ceiling. For several sickening seconds—it seemed to us minutes —*Pandora* hung in that position and then her masts snapped and she came reluctantly up to even keel again. She had turned completely over from port to starboard.

"As soon as I could tear the small hatch open, I hastened on deck with my face bruised and bleeding from several cuts. The masts were broken, the main-boom splintered, and the dinghy was washed away. We lost no time in cutting away the wreckage and freeing the boat. We drifted all that night at the mercy of the sea until the morning, when the wind changed to the south'ard. While making Hope Harbor we sighted a Norwegian whaler, and she towed us ten miles into the New Island whaling station, West Falkland Island, where she was repaired, without cost to us, through the courtesy of the whalers." [46]

More recently, the 46-foot ketch *Tzu Hang* was also turned right over and dismasted, *twice*, while trying to round Cape

171

Horn. Both times she made port under an improvised jury rig. The owner, Miles Smeeton, told the full story in his book *Once is Enough*. The *Tzu Hang* was a wooden cruising yacht with average beam and draft for her length, and not extreme in any way. It is just as absurd to condemn this type because of her misfortune as it is to damn the *Spray* model on account of what befell the *Pandora*. The incident of the *Tzu Hang* shows that capsize is certainly not confined to short, beamy pudding basins—or even "soup plates"—and *Pandora's* return to the upright indicates that the *Spray* type is not as suicidal as a lot of theorists make out. There is no doubt that it can capsize, as all boats will under severe enough conditions. There is also the possibility that it will not right itself. However, this applies to all vessels lacking infinite stability, and thus to all normal cruising yachts, since the type of craft having positive stability at all angles of heel is useless for cruising. Considerations of comfort, accommodation, and stiffness necessitate a compromise. Admittedly, the *Spray* has less stability range than most yachts, but her much higher initial stability makes capsize unlikely. The chance of meeting just the right combination of wind and sea to roll her over completely is so remote in comparison to the many other and more imminent dangers of an ocean cruise that it is hardly worth worrying about.

Indeed, the deeply ingrained notion that shallow vessels are necessarily unseaworthy has come in for some modification in recent years. Time and again, when caught offshore in whole gale conditions, yachts of the conventional deep-draft type have taken severe punishment because their very grip of the water has held them firm, like half-tide rocks, and not allowed them to give way to the full fury of the breaking seas. It is just this ability to sidle to leeward on the face of an advancing sea, so that the crest rolls harmlessly in the smooth slick left immediately to windward of the vessel, that gives vessels of shoal draft the advantage in storms at sea. The eminent Dutch naval architect M. F. Gunning recently put forward a theory dealing with the rotary movement of water particles in the advancing face of a wave, which can explain why a yacht of deep narrow sections and insufficient buoyancy buries her bows deeply in the trough of the sea and then, with her keel held by water that is not moving forward with her, is heeled even more steeply to leeward and tends to trip herself up by her own momentum.

In this regard, it is interesting to note Smeeton's comments in the Epilogue of his book on the sort of vessel he would choose "if I did it again." He wrote: "She would have broader beam than *Tzu Hang* and shallower draft, and then perhaps she would not be bowled over, if due to some misadventure I was forced to lie a-hull." [47]

Hanna's statement about the *Pandora* is about the only true and undistorted item in the whole of his article. He writes as if the sole aim of all owners of *Spray* copies has been to emulate Slocum's world trip, and in trying to put it into practice, to have met with nothing but disaster—disappearances and shipwreck. Certainly a very dramatic picture, but only a figment of Hanna's fertile imagination. Unfortunately, perhaps; otherwise the chapter on *Spray* copies might have turned out to be far more interesting—an intriguing story of many unsolved mysteries of the sea. As it is, the truth must out, and the story remains a comparatively tame one.

Only one copy of the *Spray* was wrecked. It was not on world cruise, and the accident, like many others, resulted purely from human failure and was certainly no reflection on the boat herself. Gilbert Klingel told me: "The *Basilisk* finally went ashore well after the storm we went through and did so in a rolling, but relatively calm, sea. We sighted land just at sunset and hove-to until morning, under the impression that we were still some miles from shore. What we did not know, and no charts available at that time showed, was that a very strong current ran around the north end of Great Inagua Island and the Barrier Reef which at that point extends out about one-half mile. We hit it just before dawn while we were sound asleep."

Only one copy of the *Spray* sailed around the world—and from all available records it was the only one to try. In fact, Roger Strout's original objective in his *Igdrasil* was the New Zealand Sounds, but he continued on westward and around the world as the easiest way home. Hanna's attempt to belittle her performance by implying that the voyage was largely a power trip under good conditions provoked a retort from Strout:

I had a great deal of correspondence with Hanna years ago, but I think he rather did me dirt in that item you quote from him. True, I did belittle the weather in an attempt to make some of my contemporary voyagers look ridiculous with their constant "yachtsman's gales." Anyone but a fool should realise that when one cruises for five years and from 47 degrees South to 61 North, he is bound to encounter about all the weather there is. As for running every possible mile under power, nothing could be further from the fact. The world cruise was 32,830 nautical miles during which we purchased 1,058 (U. S.) gallons of fuel. This included fuel used in the sounds of S.W. New Zealand where sailing is not practical, all fuel used during a month while under charter at Panama, and about 100 gallons that was on hand at the end of the voyage. I used my large capacity to permit me to purchase fuel where it was cheap! The Alaska cruise was somewhat different. We left Panama in March, a time when there is usually a thousand miles of calms to the westward. With gas at 10 cents a gallon what would you do there– It was 1500 miles before we caught the Trades. In Alaska we did 2600 miles of inland coastal work and only 200 of it had canvas set. In those channels it is usually calm, or else blowing a gale! Time was always pressing us that trip for we left Carolina at New Year and arrived in Seattle late in September with time out for visits in Hawaii. 13,817 nautical miles and we used 943 gallons of fuel.

Another misleading comment on the *Spray*'s seaworthiness was contained in Jacque-Yves le Toumelin's book *Kurun Around the World*. "The Americans, as loyal as they are enthusiastic, have built several sailing vessels on the exact lines of Slocum's famous *Spray*. There have been fatal accidents, and I know personally of one case of the turning over of one of these copies. There are some who maintain that this weakness was the cause of the loss of *Spray*." [48]

I was naturally interested to find out more about the copy referred to and contacted M. le Toumelin himself. He replied that the English edition of his book had omitted certain sections

174

of the original and also was not always an exact translation. The capsizing of a *Spray* copy was not a matter of his personal knowledge at all, but merely seeing a reference to the *Pandora* in an American magazine before the war. Whether deliberate or accidental, it is unfortunately misrepresentation such as this which has aided in promoting many of the widespread illusions about the *Spray* and her behavior.

The *Pandora* was the only copy of the *Spray* to turn completely over, but several others met extremely severe conditions which tested their stability. Strout wrote me of the *Igdrasil:* "At first I felt uncertain about inside ballast. After a knockdown or two while running from a cyclone in the Tasman I felt better."

He told about these in *Yachting:* "With the wind at its height we were hove to and slipping off to leeward 60 to 70 miles a day. When it eased a bit, down into the gale brackets, we ran under triple-reefed main and staysail. It was brutal driving but *Igdrasil* stood it well. Twice she was knocked down, the lee bulwarks and rail being driven a foot or more under water while it came solid clear over the cabin. Each time she shook herself dry in a matter of seconds, so I shall never again worry about the stability curve of an inside ballasted boat of this design." [49] In a letter, Strout continued:

Finally, just a hundred miles from the end of the cruise we got the real answer. While running before a strong gale at night, a heavy sea broke directly on top of us and we broached to. The starboard running light, 6 ft. off the deck, went under water and the mainsail, close-reefed, hit the water clear to the peak. I expected to swim the rest of the way. However, enough of the high cabin (well over 6 ft. headroom) was immersed to give a good righting moment, and she was up in time to get squared away before the next one. Could you ask for more? *Igdrasil's* cabin was about 30 inches high and 13 feet long. When buried a foot and a half in the water, this gives a ton and a half of lift right where it can do the most good. Most stability computations take no account of the cabin.

In this respect, it is interesting to note that shoal coasters in many parts of the world generally have high trunk cabins

175

of necessity, due to their shape. So many of these things tend to work themselves out in a design, empirically, so to speak.

Igdrasil's stability was again put to the test when a gale from dead ahead struck her between Madagascar and Durban. Strout wrote in *Yachting:* "Having the old mainsail bent I could not heave to in the usual manner without risk of losing it and I do not like to ride under mizzen and staysail. So I furled everything down tight and lay broadside to it for thirty hours. Of course, we rolled a lot and when the seas broke close inboard, it was rather disconcerting. Then the breaking sea would go completely over the ship, at the same time hurling her sidewise perhaps twenty yards. But they did no damage on deck, while chains to the rudder kept that important member from being torn off." [50]

Victor Slocum referred to the *Spray*'s ballast and her stability in his biography. "The ballast was concrete cement, stanchioned down securely to ensure it against shifting should the vessel be hove on her beam-ends. There was no outside ballast whatever. The *Spray* would have been self-righting if hove down on her beam-ends, a fact that was proven, since, by an experiment on an exact duplicate of the original boat and ballasted just like her. The test boat was hove down with mast flat to the water and when released righted herself. My father never knew of that test." [51] I wonder which copy of the *Spray* this might have been? The information does not seem to fit any already recorded, as none of them built exactly to the published lines had concrete ballast.

Slocum does not say how much ballast he carried in the *Spray*, merely that he threw overboard three tons of the cement at the Cocos Islands, "to make room and give buoyancy," and took on 30 mammoth Tridacna shells in its place. However, these three tons were probably his total ballast.

Ballast is generally considered a most important factor for stability purposes, but because of the great stability inherent in her hull shape, the *Spray* model requires much less ballast than a modern yacht of similar size. Most *Spray* copies have carried under the three tons that Slocum used, with no apparent difference in performance.

Captain Culler said:

The *Spray* model is not very critical of weight, and is no problem to ballast and keep in trim. It varies some depending on how much wood and gear are in the hull. My vessel was built with very stout sawed oak frame. On completion, the vessel was thoroughly cleaned out and cemented up to the limbers, so as to drain to a pump well. This took about a bag of cement to three parts of sand and formed the permanent ballast. I always guessed the total concrete about 375 lb. My movable ballast was extremely well spread out but I never did figure out how much I had; just trimmed her till she looked and felt right. All I was interested in was a proper and comfortable trim, which was arrived at by feel at sea, and by sight. Trim ballast was used brick, no doubt very old ones, and they were delivered alongside by a crotchety old man and sickly mule in an extremely dilapidated two wheel cart; none of the three was cooperating in the least! The load looked small, but it was enough, and I threw some out later when I installed an engine.

The *Igdrasil* carried about a ton of rock bedded in pitch. Strout told me: "I used 'Belgian Blocks'—old-time street paving blocks, which were available without cost, and pitch was cheap, being a product of the area where I built the boat. This makes a clean bilge."

The ballast of *Sirius* was more like Slocum's. She carried about 3½ tons of a mixture of steel punchings and concrete in the form of bricks. In addition, Bob Carr estimated that he had about three tons of stores.

The *Ulula* had an unusually large amount of ballast for a copy of the *Spray*—about eight tons of it, all inside and mostly lead.

In marked contrast, the *Basilisk* carried no ballast at all other than cargo, in the form of foodstuffs and similar gear, and safely weathered one of the worst storms a small vessel could experience. Gilbert Klingel wrote:

The idea that *Spray* was unsafe for ocean work is ridiculous, with or without outside ballast. After all, both Slocum and Strout sailed the boat around the world, as well as many additional miles, and were quite safe. . . . As you may know, I was once the owner of a *Spray*, and was very happy with her until I lost her in the

177

winter of 1930 off Great Inagua Island in the Bahamas. *Spray* was a wonderful ship and I'm only here today because of her. Almost any other small boat would have foundered in the gales we went through, but *Spray* (or *Basilisk* as mine was named) sailed herself through the worst storm I've ever experienced. We first met it off our fabulous Cape Hatteras, but did not get out of it until some 1,400 miles later when we were approximately 800 to 900 miles off the American coast below the tip of Florida. We spent nearly two weeks with winds never less than 40 m.p.h. and occasionally up to 90. She sailed herself through the worst of this under four-reefed main only and a fragment of jib. It was too cold and too dangerous to be on deck. During one particular storm we suffered several bad knockdowns and some mild broaches. The seas were so enormous that we had several break over the top of the mast. I had her heeled until I thought she would never come up again, time after time, but she always righted herself and kept going.

Of the Oxford *Spray*, Captain Culler said:

People are always horrified by my lack of outside ballast. Maybe the *Spray* model is capsizable, maybe not; what they forget is that all ocean and coaster vessels were generally the same—so very stiff compared to the modern yacht whose gear is under little strain when she lays down easily—and before that time came, some of the gear went. I never worried one bit about *Spray*'s stability, and more than once we got overpowered. It was always possible to reduce sail, lay to or run off as occasion demanded, with no danger of shipping a sea, which is more than can be said for some yachts.

I had some tough bouts more than once with my *Spray* but it was always up to me and not the boat. She was once in a violent line squall followed by a gale, which wrecked one of our dirigibles; she was new to me then. We were hove down quite sharply until we finally shortened sail, down to the hatches, yet there was no feeling of instability. Once when working down a river with very light air and a strong tide—there was no engine in those days—there came a white squall, with warning too, but I had to keep on sail to keep from being set ashore, and could not anchor as the squall would make it a lee shore. It struck her with little way on, the worst situation. She hove down, and then got going under the three lowers and simply blasted her way to windward. I had strong doubts about the gear holding and her ability to stay when

178

it came time; she did it in fine style with a most horrible slatting of canvas, but the gear held and with a great groaning of timbers—it could be heard above the noise of the wind—she filled away on the other tack and into the clear.

HEAVY WEATHER

Whatever is said about the *Spray*'s stability, there is ample evidence that she was well adapted for heavy weather work; in fact, it is here that the features so condemned in yachting circles showed to advantage. When the little vessel returned safely to confound the gloomy prophets who said it couldn't be done, Slocum brought proof not only of his outstanding ability as a small boat sailor, but equal proof that the *Spray* was capable of holding her own in any weather that the seas could bring.

Slocum wrote: "From the decks of stout ships in the worst gales I had made calculations as to the size and sort of ship safest for all weather and all seas." [52] The *Spray*, of course, came into Slocum's possession entirely by chance, and any resemblance to his "ideal" would have been purely coincidental. However, from his comments during and after the voyage it is clear that the *Spray* proved to be eminently suitable.

The supreme test of the *Spray*'s buoyancy and stability took place when she was struck by a gigantic tidal wave off the Patagonian coast. She had three reefs tucked in at the time:

While the sloop was reaching under short sail, a tremendous wave, the culmination, it seemed, of many waves, rolled down upon her in a storm, roaring as it came. I had only a moment to get all sail down and myself up on the peak halliards, out of danger, when I saw the mighty crest towering masthead-high above me. The mountain of water submerged my vessel. She shook in every timber and reeled under the weight of the sea, but rose quickly out of it, and rode grandly over the rollers that followed. It may have been a minute that from my hold in the rigging I could see no part of the *Spray*'s hull. . . . the incident, which filled me with fear, was only one more test of the *Spray*'s worthiness. It reassured me against rude Cape Horn. [53]

179

Slocum referred to the event again in a letter to a friend, dated February 16, 1896, which was first published in the *Standard* of Buenos Aires, and later by *The Yachtsman:* "We experienced a gale off the Gulf of St. George, and a tidal wave that shook the little *Spray* and tried her to her utmost capacity. It would have tried any ship." [54]

Slocum carried a sea anchor on the *Spray* for use in heavy weather. Shortly before his departure from Boston, he said to reporters: "When it blows too hard I shall get out my sea anchor, batten everything down tight, and go below for a sleep and let the gale blow itself out." [55] In his biography, Victor Slocum said: "The sea anchor he always had and frequently used," [56] but, strangely enough, Slocum only referred to it twice in his book. The first occasion it proved handy was after leaving Gloucester at the beginning of the voyage, when Slocum stopped over a ledge in thirty fathoms of water to supplement his provisions with some fresh fish. He baited a hook and "put out a sea-anchor that would hold her head to windward." [57] The only other time it was mentioned was two days before the end of the voyage, and then it was put to a more fitting use. Off Fire Island Slocum met a tornado

which, an hour earlier, had swept over New York city with lightning that wrecked buildings and sent trees flying about in splinters; even ships at docks had parted their moorings and smashed into other ships, doing great damage. It was the climax storm of the voyage, but I saw the unmistakable character of it in time to have all snug aboard and receive it under bare poles. Even so, the sloop shivered when it struck her, and she heeled over unwillingly on her beam ends; but rounding to, with a sea-anchor ahead, she righted and faced out the storm.[58]

Only two copies of the *Spray* used a sea anchor. One was the *Basilisk*, Klingel reporting that "she rode very nicely to it." The other was the *Pandora*, which had occasion to put out a sea anchor in fierce winds and raging seas on the way to New Zealand. However, it was not so successful. *Rudder* stated: "For a time the yawl rode safely and then some of her gear carried away, the result of the sea-anchor failing to keep *Pandora*'s head to the sea. Next the anchor carried away and with it went a large section of the starboard bulwarks. With the aid of a reefed trysail *Pandora* rode out the gale. . . .[59]

Most *Spray* copies have been content to heave to without the assistance of a sea anchor. Yachts with a good length of straight keel will usually lie-to quietly in most weathers, looking after themselves unattended and giving their crews a rest in comparative comfort. The *Spray* was one of this type.

Strout wrote of the *Igdrasil:* "I can't say that I like gales but they do let us catch up on sleep! Under close reefed main only, with boom well off and tiller amidships, the ship lies six points off the wind and requires not the slightest attention. We go to sleep until a decrease in wind starts things slatting." [60] He added in a letter: "Heaving to, she does not like the sheet checked in hard, in fact the boom, when shortened for ketch rig, should be outboard of the rail for best results. Set thus, the rudder may be central or even unshipped, and she rides perfectly. . . . She would not heave to under mizzen and headsails."

Gilbert Klingel said: "*Basilisk* hove-to very nicely and did not make too much leeway and did not slap and bang around very much. She did not heave to ideally under jib and mizzen no matter how I trimmed them."

Of the Oxford *Spray*, Captain Culler wrote: "Hove to she was most easy."

With increasing wind and breaking seas, there comes a time when a boat can no longer be held into it by drags, sea anchors, riding sails, or any other means. The only recourse then is to run before it. It is under such extreme conditions that the ability to run clean and true may mean the difference between success and disaster. Of course, a heavy and beamy ship like the *Spray* is slower running off than a light, narrow one, but it is in this very slowness that her safety lies. When running in heavy weather, her great displacement and beam minimize the danger of broaching to. On the other hand, a ship with fine racing lines will travel fast before a gale of wind, with risk of approaching her critical speed and becoming unstable. When running off before a following sea, such a yacht will also roll violently due to her fine sections and heavy ballast

181

keel. This regular rail-dipping roll downwind—lurch and pause, lurch and pause—is one of the most tiring characteristics of the modern ocean racer. Apart from being exhausting to the crew, it is also a dangerous fault, as the yacht creates her own deep and heavy wave system that can make her almost impossible to control in bad weather. In contrast, a beamy vessel like the *Spray* has little roll and a clean water flow, and is far steadier with following wind and sea. Under these conditions too, the advantages of a full bow as well as a full beam should be obvious, in the light of the *Tzu Hang*. Fine ends may look nice in harbor; out at sea they are merely asking for trouble.

The *Spray*'s seaworthiness was put to the test after she had successfully negotiated the passage through the Strait of Magellan. The wind was fair from the northeast, and she ran with a free sheet. The wind shifted to the southwest, then suddenly back to the northwest, and blew with terrific force:

The *Spray*, stripped of her sails, then bore off under bare poles. No ship in the world could have stood up against so violent a gale . . . for my present safety the only course lay in keeping her before the wind. . . . She was running now with a reefed forestaysail, the sheets flat amidship. I paid out two long ropes to steady her course and to break combing seas astern, and I lashed the helm amidship. In this trim she ran before it, shipping never a sea. Even while the storm raged at its worst, my ship was wholesome and noble. My mind as to her seaworthiness was put at ease for aye. . . .

The first day of the storm gave the *Spray* her actual test in the worst sea that Cape Horn or its wild regions could afford, and in no part of the world could a rougher sea be found than at this particular point, namely, off Cape Pillar, the grim sentinel of the Horn.[61]

Slocum later said to reporters in Sydney: "The storm was the fiercest I ever saw, and several large vessels that were in it were dismasted. . . . Such seas I never experienced during my life, but the *Spray* behaved grandly and rode over them like a bird." [62]

The *Spray*'s merit for running in strong winds and rough

seas was also demonstrated by her copies. Captain Culler wrote about his *Spray:* "Her model was the best running off that I've ever been in—I trusted her before the wind like no other."

Roger Strout told of approaching Durban before a northeast gale:

Bucking this was the tide at half ebb, only a day after springs. The moon had not risen so I could not see how heavily the bar was breaking or I would not have tried it.

We had been running under headsails only for some time, so I took in the jib, sheeted the staysail amidships to keep her paid off and started the engine for quicker steering. In the first big trough, we lost sight of the 282-foot lighthouse three-fourths of a mile away! Then *Igdrasil* got on the crest of a breaking sea and rode it like a surf board while the engine roared in a vain effort to keep up with the propeller. Losing that one, there was a period of control under power before the next one caught us for another ride.

I had expected to be swept from end to end and so had everything on deck securely lashed, but to my unbounded amazement not a single sea came aboard. In spite of her much criticized transom, *Igdrasil* showed no tendency to broach to as we raced on toward the jetties. . . . The port captain even got out his anemometer records to prove that it was blowing 50 miles an hour at the time we passed the instrument.[63]

Heading north toward Kodiak Island on their Alaskan trip, the Strouts met with a storm from the southwest: "the radio marine bulletin from N.P.G. reported a storm centre south of Kodiak. That was right in our path, but I could not waste the first good wind in days. So, under headsails and mizzen, we took the gale on the quarter and headed right for the centre of the disturbance, making about 140 miles a day, while we stayed snug below. *Igdrasil* runs perfectly without attention under these conditions." [64]

However, storm conditions are not always as good as this, and the crew of the *Pandora* had a different story to tell of their Tasman crossing. Thomas Fleming Day wrote:

Her navigators unite in stating that the weather encountered during the run to Auckland was the worst of the entire voyage and it

183

was a badly battered craft that finally ran into the shelter of the harbor. When ten days out from Sydney the little *Pandora* was wallowing through a sea that threatened every minute to swamp her. On August 28th the wind, which had been whipping up the sea at whole gale speed, increased with great suddenness to a hurricane, and by noon the boat was down to bare poles and shipping water with every jump she made in the high-running sea. She finally shipped a heavy green sea which swept her length and flooded her cabin. The yawl listed to such a degree that for a few seconds she hung on her beam ends and then slowly righted. Captain Arapakis was at the wheel. He saw the advancing wall of water and clung to a wooden bar until the flood passed, leaving him breathless, wet, and exhausted. Captain Blythe, who had been caught in the small cabin, was bruised and battered, as the sea set him and most of the fixtures tumbling about in the small space. The sea carried away the port bulwarks, and sent overboard a cask of meat which had been lashed to the deck.[65]

HELM

The *Spray*, like many older type working vessels, had a long, straight keel, and was therefore slower on the helm than a modern yacht. However, she was not the complete sluggard most people imagine. Slocum was heading for an anchorage in St. Nicholas Bay in the Strait of Magellan when the staysail sheet parted in turbulent seas. He rushed forward "to see instantly a dark cliff ahead and breakers so close under the bows that I felt surely lost. . . . I sprang aft again, unheeding the flapping sail, and threw the wheel over, expecting, as the sloop came down into the hollow of a wave, to feel her timbers smash under me on the rocks. But at the touch of her helm she swung clear of the danger, and in the next moment she was in the lee of the land." [66]

One day, Slocum's brother Ornan went sailing in the *Spray* out of Vineyard Haven. Walter Magnes Teller told the story in *The Search for Captain Slocum:* "The captain set the course too close to the rocks around West Chop. Ornan, who was at the wheel, warned that they were in danger, but his brother was calling the orders. When, finally, Slocum realized that he really was in too close, he shouted in a voice like the last trumpet 'Hard over!' Ornan responded with such sudden and vigorous action that the captain fell full length on the deck, flat on his back." [67] Surely no sign this of a sluggish helm!

Archibald Roosevelt wrote of his trip on the *Spray:* "Of course, she was slow on the helm to anybody accustomed to using our racing yachts or deep keel cutters. However, for a long-keeled boat she was very handy going about and I never recalled that she got in stays."

Harold Smith was not so complimentary. "From a yachtsman's standpoint *Spray* was exceedingly slow on the helm, also exceedingly slow in going about. Furthermore, she had to be sailed about rather than just *put* about. If she was tacked suddenly without letting her off to get a good full she was likely to miss stays and get badly in irons."

K. B. Johnstone had similar experience with the St. Kilda *Spray.* He wrote: "She had to be backwinded on the headsails to put her about, and not always successfully. She needed a lot of sea room to handle her in."

I saw this copy in Melbourne some years ago and noticed how small the rudder was. The whole after top end of the *Spray*'s typical old-style "barn door" rudder had been cut away and rounded off in the modern way. It struck me that this "beautification" treatment might have had a lot to do with the vessel's poor performance.

Other owners of copies also commented on the helm, but their reports were more favorable.

Henry Longmore said: "In light airs she was a bit of a cow going about, but the added depth of keel may well have had something to do with this."

Horace Schmahl found much the same thing: "The *Island Trader* responds extremely well to the helm. However, she needs a great deal of rudder way to come about. When we are tacking at a light breeze I generally have a crewman back the jib in order to facilitate her coming over. The vessel has never failed to come about except during very light winds."

Herr Leisegang wrote of his *Heimat:* "To be sure she was

185

slow to come about—only to be expected with a long, deep keel—but nevertheless answered the helm well. At our place in Berlin I often had to make cruises through the narrow waterways in which only two boat lengths were available for tacking. . . ." With a short, steep sea, however, it was a different story; Leisegang continued: "She was difficult to tack in a short, high sea, due more, I believe, to the excessive ballast which was given to the ship, combined with the tall mast, than to the full bow. The extra weight spoiled her performance and the original *Spray* would have been better. In a rough sea, my *Spray* often came almost to a standstill when she tacked."

Most owners of *Spray* copies seem to agree on a slow helm, but nevertheless a sure one; whether this is a weakness or not is largely a matter of opinion. Gilbert Klingel seemed to think it was, under certain conditions:

The greatest fault of *Spray* was her slowness in answering the helm. In a choppy sea, she was the very devil to bring about and most of the time I had to take her around the other way. In a long, heavy ocean roll, I rarely had any problems in this respect. You may expect trouble coming about, but this is the penalty you pay for having a perfectly balanced boat capable of runs of hundreds of miles without a hand on the wheel. However, I found a considerable difference in *Basilisk* when she was light and when she was heavily loaded. With a good cargo aboard there was no particular trouble coming about except in an extremely choppy sea.

This raises an interesting point. No doubt the extra loading gave a greater momentum and enabled her to carry more way on through the water when tacking. Klingel continued: "The boat, as she is designed, is too light anyway and should carry a little weight with her to bring her to her proper water line." *Basilisk*'s draft when light was 4 feet, and loaded, 4 feet 6 inches. The Oxford *Spray* had a 4-foot 6-inch draft when light and near 5 feet loaded. Culler agreed about the desirability of extra weight. He wrote:

In regard to the apparent difference in my vessel's draft and Slocum's original, the hulls are actually the same. The approximate draft of 5 ft. is due to the vessel being in sailing trim with gear aboard. Probably Mower figured the draft as the "light draft" when he took the lines off. Working vessel design, especially in the smaller vessels in the old days at least, took little account of the actual draft in practice. It varied with loading and use, and was of no matter except for the vessel to fulfil her purpose. The vessels were not designed to a set of rules, and their weight varied a good deal, even among similar craft. . . . I never really cared just what the draft was, so long as she was in good trim. It was not a critical point with her, though the fore and aft trim was. In spite of the full bow, the model does not take too kindly to trimming by the head. She needed to be kept by the stern for best sailing.

The *Ulula* provided a good example of this very thing. Charles Hinman reported that the vessel's fore-and-aft trim affected her performance. After restowing seven hundred-weight of ballast from the forecastle to beneath the engine, he noticed an improvement in helm response when tacking.

Apart from a boat's trim, another factor with an important influence on the helm is the form of the run. Where there is pronounced fuss at the stern caused by the drag and wave-making tendency of a hull with heavy buttocks, the rudder may be in such broken and aerated water that its efficiency is impaired. A clean run certainly improves its performance under both sail and power. Mrs. Culler wrote of the Oxford *Spray:* "She draws most of her water aft and has a long easy run beginning well forward. This enables her to leave an easy wake under sail and to handle like a tug under power. She'll turn in her own length and constantly astounds deck tenders by her maneuvering." [68] Captain Culler added in a letter:

The *Spray* model handles extremely well around docks and close places under power. She takes very modest power in smooth water and at moderate speed. I had three different engines over a long period; they all were 40 h.p. more or less, and were mostly run to develop about 25 h.p. in smooth conditions, sometimes less. A 22-inch two-blade wheel was always used, though the pitch was altered to suit the different engines. . . . Outside of a full-powered boat of excellent model, I've never seen a boat that would handle like *Spray*. She is just as good at that as in other things. I've never mentioned this much, as those interested were not so concerned in the power angle. *Spray* could and did make the modern auxiliary, and power boat too, look like junk when it came to handling around docks.

About sailing performance, Culler said:

My ship was excellent in stays; old-timers used to remark on how handy she was. True, I backed the jib—with the sheet fast in the usual leeward position it became aback as a matter of course when the helm was put down and it was then let draw in the time-honored and traditional manner when the vessel's head was far enough around. This is the standard coastal maneuver the world over, or was, when there were ships. I did not know any better until I was so foolish as to go in modern yachts; if you so much as let go the helm to light a pipe, they flash around on the other tack. Suppose this is now considered a wonderful virtue, but I like the old steady way.

Roger Strout had similar views: "As for coming about, a deep-water boat *should* be slow. It is an inevitable concomitant of selfsteering ability. Only once in five years did *Igdrasil* fail to come about when desired and that time wasn't her fault. In normal sailing she handled as fast as I could wish, while under power she turned like a jack rabbit. Remember, the snappy handling racer makes the worst possible cruising vessel." He might also have added that a bit more room to maneuver in is hardly of much importance—there is no lack of space in ocean cruising.

SPEED

Looking at the *Spray*, one tends to form quite a false impression of her speed. Compared to modern yachts she looks like a slow old barge, and of course she is, under normal sailing conditions. However, with sufficient wind, she could really get along. Her appearance is deceptive; the underwater lines are what count so far as speed is concerned, and hers were very easy indeed. Certainly she rolled up a big bow wave when going fast, but since the streamlines from the stem are

188

under the boat, not around her, the great beam does not have the paralyzing effect one might expect. Further, the wide flat transom is not a beauty feature by modern standards, but it does not adversely affect her performance.

Captain Culler commented: "Yes, *Spray* made a big bow wave, especially when going fast. What she did not do was pull a huge mound of water after her at any speed, which is the fault I find with most modern craft. This, I think, was the reason she steered so well in a following sea; certainly she never caused a sea to break."

Gilbert Klingel wrote: "*Basilisk* left very little wake when going fast."

Strout said: "Neither does the broad transom pull the ocean after it as they expect. In fact, the dinghy towed astern throws a far greater wake than does the vessel at the same speed!" [69]

On Slocum's world cruise, the *Spray* sailed more than 46,000 nautical miles, which, with her actual sailing time of 462 days, gives an average speed for the whole voyage of a little over four knots. She made trade-wind passages of 100 to 150 miles a day without any trouble; this compares favorably with most other boats of her size and is quite fast enough for anyone who is not racing.

The *Spray*'s best performance was during the first week out in the North Atlantic. With a fresh northwesterly breeze, she was "heading southeast, and making about eight knots her very best work. . . . July 10, eight days at sea, the *Spray* was twelve hundred miles east of Cape Sable. One hundred and fifty miles a day for so small a vessel must be considered good sailing. It was the greatest run the *Spray* ever made before or since in so few days." [70]

Even under reefs, she made good time. After leaving Samoa, "a sudden burst of the trades brought her down to close reefs, and she reeled off one hundred and eighty-four miles the first day, of which I counted forty miles of current in her favor." [71]

Some of the *Spray*'s ocean runs were: Thursday Island to the Cocos Islands, 2,700 miles, 23 days; Cape Town to St. Helena, 1,700 miles, 16 days; St. Helena to Ascension, 7 days;

from Ascension to Grenada, she averaged more than 110 miles a day; around Cape St. Roque with a leading wind she made 180 miles a day, with 40 off for current. Her fast runs were not confined to the open sea. Sailing up the Queensland coast from Danger Point to the Whitsunday Pass, within sight of the land most of the time, the *Spray* made 110 miles a day for five days—not bad going for a 37-footer so close inshore.

Copies of the *Spray* also put up quite a good performance. Strout stated:

Contrary to most yachtsmen's opinions *Igdrasil* was not slow. Her best 24 hour run was 204 nautical miles while passing Cape Hatteras in a strong southwesterly breeze with the mizzen furled. About 25 miles of this was current. She did better than 170 without benefit of current on perhaps half a dozen occasions. More representative would be these good runs: Kingston, Jamaica, to Panama, wind, sea and current abeam, full sail never set, 525 miles in 4 days 1 hour; Christmas Island to Keeling Cocos as sailed, 540 miles in 94 hours; Keeling to Rodriguez, 2,000 miles in 16½ days.

The *Igdrasil* did the Durban to Cape Town passage in ten days, and averaged 100 miles a day from Ascension to Barbados in spite of the doldrums. In *Yachting*, Strout told about leaving Whitsunday Island in the Great Barrier Reef in a freshening wind: "We were down to headsails and mizzen. Even under this short canvas, *Igdrasil* reefed off 135 miles in 22 hours.[72]

Of his *Spray*, Captain Culler said: "Best speed I ever got out of her was eight knots even—did it on three occasions, twice in smooth water, where one could overcarry on sail, and once coastwise between buoys, so think it's about top for that vessel."

Gilbert Klingel commented: "I never measured *Basilisk's* speed very accurately; however, I covered 1,800 miles in two weeks flat and out of this time I spent two days under sea anchor and hove-to. The rest of it was sailing with winds on the quarter and three reefed main and full jib, so I imagine I was averaging 150/160 miles a day or better. This was under very high wind conditions."

Captain Clinton Baverstock told about a cruise on the *Saga-*

190

more in the Bahamas in 1954. "We ran into very rough weather in the Gulf Stream on our return trip but as the wind was on the beam, we made an average of seven knots under reefed main, jib, and jigger." Neal Small added: "I am sure of seven knots and I think she might do eight under good conditions."

The schooner *Island Trader* was not as fast, thus illustrating the difference between *Foam I* and *II*, already mentioned. Horace Schmahl wrote: "Her maximum speed, which she attains with all canvas up at a following wind, is 6½ knots."

Charles Hinman said that for so short and beamy a boat the *Ulula* had a fair turn of speed. "In anything but the lightest of airs I used to base my dead reckoning on an average speed of 5.8 knots."

The *Starbound* was about nine feet longer on the waterline than the *Spray* and, naturally, was faster. "I have obtained speeds of 9.25 knots with a square sail and raffee," reported Kenneth Whitteker.

The *Heimat* was another enlarged copy and was also very fast. Herr Leisegang wrote: "She had an excellent run and wake, which was the best evidence of her model. . . . The *Heimat* was very fast, much faster for example than seven 24-tonners built at that time in the German dockyards and rigged as ketches. As far as I know, three at least of these were sent to Australia. As to her top speed, I would say 11 to 12 miles."

Spray's large sail area stood by her even in light winds, so long as they were following. One day on the Atlantic crossing the wind was light and the sea smooth, and "the *Spray*, with a great mainsail bellying even to light winds, was just skipping along as nimbly as one could wish." [73] Here the wind was on the quarter. When it was from ahead, of course, things were very different; those very features which made the *Spray* such a good vessel when running off, naturally enough proved a disadvantage when close hauled. A short, choppy sea, together with a light head wind provide the worst conditions for boats of the *Spray* type.

In *Yachting Monthly*, H. O. Cooper wrote: "I should be very much obliged if you could let me know whether any boat has been built as a yacht on the lines of *Spray* and if she was at all successful in English waters." The editor, who was apparently unaware of the Rochester *Spray*, replied: "No boat, so far as we can ascertain, has been built in England on these lines. The short seas around the British coasts place excessive beam at a disadvantage, hence its unpopularity with designers in this country. In open sea work where very short seas are not constantly met, greater beam has its advantages." [74]

The bluff-bowed, beamy types certainly do not shine to windward, especially in a coastal chop, but that does not prevent them making a reasonable showing. They are not necessarily condemned to be hopelessly slow—it depends very largely on their underwater body. Some of the old-style beamy working vessels of Europe put up quite a creditable performance under such conditions. The Dutch boeiers are relatively just as beamy as the *Spray*, even more so, but their behavior is surprising. L. Francis Herreshoff stated in *Rudder*: "You may be astonished at the full lines of these Boeiers, but they are a perfected ancient type and descended from the first yachts or *jaghts* in the world. The general type has not changed much in three or more centuries. . . . It does seem amazing, but these fine little vessels seem to tromp the waves under them instead of cutting through them and really go to windward remarkably well in a sea." [75]

However, not all beamy boats can measure up to the boeiers. There must have been many times when the *Spray* tried even Slocum's patience. Shortly before closing the Spanish coast, she encountered a gale from the north. It kicked up heavy seas and Slocum had to shorten sail. Reaching under close reefed main and bobbed jib, one day she made only fifty-one miles on her course. Crossing the doldrums in the Atlantic, between the northeast and southeast trades, the *Spray* was harassed by squalls, calms, and baffling seas and currents. In ten days, she made only 300 miles. Slocum told of meeting light headwinds on the New South Wales coast: "with a good stock of books on board, I fell to reading day and night, leaving this pleasant occupation merely to trim sails or tack, or to lie down and rest, while the *Spray* nibbled at the miles." [76]

There is no doubt that in light airs and close windward work, the *Spray* is simply not to be compared to modern yachts. Horace Schmahl's comments about his *Island Trader* could apply to this type of vessel generally. "The *Island Trader* is primarily a heavy weather boat. She does not like light winds. We found her performing at her very best in a 25-m.p.h. breeze."

Captain Culler sailed the Oxford *Spray* a lot on Chesapeake Bay, where the winds are mainly light, and through the Inland Waterway. He fitted a topsail which proved very useful, as Mrs. Culler described in *Rudder:* "Our topsail is our special pet. It contains 130 square feet and clews aloft, coaster style, by means of a clewline and buntline leading to the deck. It can be set or taken in from the deck even before the wind. We find it especially useful running the inland waterways when the banks are often high, blanketing the wind from our mainsail." [77]

One *Spray* copy, the *Ulula*, was noteworthy for her unusual performance in light conditions. Charles Hinman said: "She did not even stop in a very light air and short sea. . . . Most remarkable for so heavily built a boat she was marvelous in a very light air. She would keep steerage way on her when there was so little wind that you could walk around the deck carrying an unshielded lighted candle. I remember four hours of that in Barnstable Bay." The *Ulula* carried a lot of inside ballast; perhaps that had something to do with it.

Generally, however, the *Spray* must be considered as far from ideal for light going and the usual windward work. Here is where the modern yacht scores. But, of course, you can't have it both ways—"You pays your money and takes your choice!"

HANDLING

On her ocean crossings, the *Spray* was a good passage maker, and the longer the run, the better she did. In view of her huge tonnage and sail area compared to most boats her length, many yachtsmen find it hard to understand how she could be sailed so fast, or even handled at all, by one man. Looking at the *Spray*, she is certainly quite a lump of a boat, and you tend to forget she is only a 37 footer. "How big a crew does she need?" is a frequent question. However, to compare the *Spray* with the average yacht is hardly fair to either. Modern craft require much larger crews because they usually put a big effort and strain on them to keep going. These things are so commonplace that they are taken for granted.

True, the *Spray*'s rig was heavy; Slocum himself said "it was no small matter to hoist the large sail. . . ." [78] His son Garfield wrote: "It was a job for two people. The mainsail and gaff were heavy. I know it was hard for him to raise it when he was alone." [79] Slocum also said "the hard work, too, of getting the sloop under way every morning was finished, I had hoped, when she cleared the Strait of Magellan." [80] The *Spray* was, of course, an ocean cruiser, pure and simple; certainly she was not very suited for prolonged single-handed harbor or coastal work, with its continual raising and lowering of gear.

Approaching Durban, the *Spray* was sighted by the signalman from the bluff station. When she was within eight miles, he reported: "The *Spray* is shortening sail; the mainsail was reefed and set in ten minutes. One man is doing all the work." [81] This item of news was printed three minutes later in a Durban morning paper, which was handed to Slocum when he arrived in port. He said:

I could not verify the time it had taken to reef the sail, for, as I have already said, the minute-hand of my timepiece was gone. I only knew that I reefed as quickly as I could.

. . . undue estimates have been made of the amount of skill and energy required to sail a sloop of even the *Spray*'s small tonnage. I heard a man who called himself a sailor say that "it would require three men to do what it was claimed" that I did alone, and what I found perfectly easy to do over and over again; and I have heard that others made similar nonsensical remarks, adding that I would work myself to death.[82]

194

Such a comment was not merely the modesty of a superlative seaman; the *Spray* was not a hard boat to handle. Slocum stated: "She is very easily managed, even in a breeze." [83] Later, in a letter written not long after setting out, he said: "I experience no inconvenience in working the sloop alone. . . ." [84] To yachtsmen, viewing her great mainsail in the light of their usual mad scramble on a tossing, steep deck, this is a mystery. Ease of handling, however, is determined more by the type of rigging and gear and its workability than by the mere size of the boat or its sail area.

Mrs. Culler said of the Oxford *Spray:* "Pete and I have no trouble at all in managing her alone. Of course, before I came along, he sailed her single-handed as did J. Slocum. This is possible because she is simply and sensibly rigged. There are no elaborate gadgets or backstays requiring adjustment and she steers herself to a large extent." [85] Captain Culler added in a letter: "Never found the mainsail to be a monster; in fact it was much easier than these synthetic slippery things of much less area that they make now, with no proper gear to handle them. . . . The ship was very easy to reef, as she ran steadily with little attention and was a steady platform from which to work. This is far more important than size of sail, for if one is on his ear being thrown about, even a dish cloth is hard to handle."

The importance of workable gear for easy handling is nowhere better illustrated than with ground tackle. In E. G. Martin and John Irving's *Cruising and Ocean Racing*, R. Maclean-Buckley spoke of the selection of a singlehanded cruiser. "The maximum size must be determined by the ease with which one man can handle his ground tackle. The probable limit is about 30 tons. To many this would seem far too large, but two of the most successful single-handed cruisers in this country have done the greater part of their cruising in yachts of over 30 tons. With well-chosen gear . . . and well-planned anchor davits or catheads, ground tackle in a yacht of this size can be handled far more easily than those who have never tried it would suppose." [86]

Mrs. Culler detailed the handling of their anchor gear on the Oxford *Spray*:

Her ground tackle is another source of wonder to others and comfort to us. There is nothing so conducive to a peaceful night's sleep as the knowledge that you have a good hook overboard and another handy should a blow come. We carry three anchors. Our starboard bower weighs 175 pounds, the port 150 pounds, and the kedge 75 pounds, all of the old-fashioned stock pattern. To the yachtsman who is in the habit of hauling up a 50-pounder with his hands our great hooks, to say nothing of our 40 fathoms of ½ inch chain, look like physical impossibilities; when, however, you are sailing the year round in a 15-ton home it's nice to know you have some means of holding her where you want her. Incidentally, she was glad to have all of her 400 pounds of iron overboard in the September '38 hurricane. These large hooks are workable simply because they are properly rigged. We don't try to pull them up by hand. We use a gypsy windlass to raise the hook, occasionally putting on the power to break her out. Then we have cat heads, another good old coaster practice scorned by yachtsmen. A cat stop, running through the cat head, slips through the ring of the anchor and is used to pull the ring to the cat head. Then a large iron fishhook, attached to a tackle, is slipped under a fluke and used as a purchase to raise the anchor so that it rests on the rail. The hook and tackle are kept handy, lashed to the starboard rigging. To let go a hook in a hurry it is only necessary to loose the cat stop and stand on the end of it. Then using a handspike from the windlass as a lever, plop the anchor overboard letting the stop go at the same time. Many a time we have come to a flying moor in the New Harbor at Block Island with everything on her and the wind cracking down as it usually does there and you can't do that without a good sized chunk of iron on the bottom.[87]

Another factor contributing to the *Spray*'s ease of handling and her fast runs was her balance. Had she not possessed the ability to sail herself for days and weeks at a time, Slocum's performance would have been utterly impossible. Just take any of his trade wind passages and figure the average miles per day made good. It will be immediately apparent that such averages could not be maintained with the sails furled for rest or sleep each night. It was the *Spray*'s excellent balance which above all else was responsible for her good passages.

Victor Slocum commented on the *Spray*'s Atlantic crossing: "The Captain felt by this time that he had a self-steering ship, so his mind was at rest as far as future navigation was concerned. It was like having three extra men on board standing regular watches." [88]

Bound down the South American coast after leaving Rio de Janeiro, Slocum wrote: "Coasting along on this part of the voyage, I observed that while some of the small vessels I fell in with were able to outsail the *Spray* by day, they fell astern of her by night. To the *Spray* day and night were the same; to the others clearly there was a difference." [89] That modest comment sums up the secret of the *Spray*'s success.

Of the passage from Juan Fernandez to the Marquesas, Slocum said: "My time was all taken up those days—not by standing at the helm; no man, I think, could stand or sit and steer a vessel round the world: I did better than that; for I sat and read my books, mended my clothes, or cooked my meals and ate them in peace. . . ." [90] In a letter written about this trip later at the Cocos Islands, he added: "I was then 43 days out and had not lost 6 hours rest. But the vessel had sailed at her top speed all that time or all the time that the wind blew hard." [91]

The *Spray*'s balance helped her speed in another way. When running before the wind most yachts need a lot of helm to keep them straight on their course; but, in the *Spray*, there was no need for that continual fighting of the rudder, with its resultant braking effect, which generally is such a tiring feature of steering downwind.

In addition, the *Spray*'s buoyancy allowed her to run safely in a sea that would tax another craft severely. Mrs. Culler stated: "Her best sailing point is running free. Due to her full bow and easy run she holds her head up and you can force her before the wind." [92] Yes—the *Spray* could stand up to her canvas; she could be "druv," as the fishermen say. In heavy weather, it is usually the crew which gives out before the boat, and it was the *Spray*'s extreme buoyancy and comfort which enabled her to keep going where another boat would be burying herself. Slocum was able to drive her day and night without fatigue, where others were too worn out from discomfort to get the best out of their craft. This was the reason her passages compare favorably with those of faster vessels.

There were many stretches of ocean over which Slocum in the *Spray*, and Gerbault in the *Firecrest*, sailed at about the same time of the year. The *Firecrest* was designed as a racer and was undoubtedly the faster boat, but Gerbault's passages were quite uniformly twice as long as Slocum's. Some typical examples are: Cocos Islands to Rodriguez—*Spray* 16 days, *Firecrest* 31 days; Cape Town to St. Helena—*Spray* 16 days, *Firecrest* 32 days; St. Helena to Ascension—*Spray* 7 days, *Firecrest* 14 days. A fast boat does not necessarily make fast passages at sea, particularly when sailed by one man. For the lone voyager in the open ocean, speed depends as much on comfort as on anything else, and it was comfort that lay behind the *Spray*'s great runs. This comprised many things—stiffness, easy motion, dryness, and roominess.

The *Spray*'s stability not only helped make her an easy boat to handle; it also contributed much to the comfort and well-being of the crew. She was, in every sense of the word, a *livable* boat.

Roger Strout wrote: "Yachtsmen often scoff at *Igdrasil*'s great beam, but it makes her sail on her bottom, not on one edge as yachts are wont to do. This is greatly appreciated by my wife when preparing meals. The galley stays right side up and she doesn't have to do the cooking on the bias." [93]

Mrs. Culler enlarged on the importance of stiffness from the cook's point of view:

This stiffness is highly important in extended cruising, as it ensures a dry, comfortable cabin and substantial meals just when they are most needed. My greatest culinary success was the production of a roast, mashed potatoes, corn pudding, and creamed cauliflower, served steaming hot immediately after a three-hour beat around Race Pt. into Provincetown at the end of a day's run from Nantucket.

198

Many a pie and cake has come out of our Shipmate to amaze the usual race-boat sailor who has learned to put up with a can of beans or a cold ham sandwich. If you're going to live aboard a boat as we do you might as well do it in comfort.[94]

MOTION

No small boat is comfortable at sea; but some are rather less uncomfortable than others. This relative comfort is very important for ocean cruising, since the strain of long passages is considerably reduced when the motion is easy.

Because of her flat sides and bottom, the *Spray* is often likened to a barge, and assumed to be jerky and uncomfortable. John Hanna pointed out that this was not necessarily so:

The *Spray* was very heavily built, and to that owed her easy motion. You have often heard, from men who know nothing of the laws of motion and less about the behaviour of boats, that "because of her hard bilge *Spray* had a quick, jerky roll." Of course, much less than 46,000 miles of quick, jerky rolling would kill any man ever born, and Slocum was not a superman by any means. It is true that *Spray*'s form tended to quick recovery. *Also*, however, it is true that there is no motion, not even the swing of the planets around the sun, that cannot be slowed down by loading it with appropriately directed resistance. Her hull weight was *Spray*'s brake on quick action.[95]

Slocum mentioned the *Spray*'s motion several times. Out from Gibraltar in the northeast trades, he wrote: "The wind . . . blew a steady but moderate gale, and the sea, though agitated into long rollers, was not uncomfortably rough or dangerous, and while sitting in my cabin I could hardly realize that any sea was running at all so easy was the long swinging motion of the sloop over the waves." [96]

A little later on, after leaving the Canaries, the *Spray* had the wind dead aft, with her boom broad off: "The wind freshened. . . . Her mast now bent under a strong, steady pressure, and her bellying sail swept the sea as she rolled scuppers under, courtseying to the waves. These rolling waves thrilled me as they tossed my ship, passing quickly under

199

her keel. This was grand sailing." [97] Scuppers under, for the *Spray*, amounted to only 15 degrees heel.

On the passage to St. Helena: "March 31 the fresh southeast wind had come to stay. The *Spray* was running under a single-reefed mainsail, a whole jib, and a flying jib besides. . . . The sloop was again doing her work smoothly, hardly rolling at all, but just leaping along among the white horses. . . ." [98]

On his return from a winter cruise to the West Indies in 1908, Slocum said to reporters: "I left Block Island in a snorting gale of wind, and in four day's time I hadn't spilled any water out of an open bucket!" [99]

Harold Smith recalled: "*Spray* was by all odds one of the easiest vessels on which I have ever sailed. She was easy in a seaway; she pitched with a slow motion, rolled scarcely at all. Even in a strong seaway, it was possible to walk forward without hanging on."

Archibald Roosevelt wrote: "She had a very pleasant motion even in the choppy seas around Point Judith."

Horace Schmahl commented in detail:

The *Island Trader* does not roll as much as she pitches and even her pitching motion is by far less than that found in other broad-beamed cruising vessels in the area. She is an extremely comfortable boat. Indicative of this statement is the fact that my family and I rode out the hurricane Cleo aboard the *Island Trader* in the notoriously rough waters off Block Island, R. I. Hurricane Cleo had gusts of wind up to 140 m.p.h. and the water off Block Island is supposedly the roughest on the eastern part of the Atlantic seaboard. We were weathering this storm with a storm jib and the flying jib set as a trysail on the mainmast. We sailed the *Island Trader* from Block Island to Newport, R. I., in this holocaust without discomfort and without getting overly wet. Our children range in age from six to fourteen years and they remained with us on deck throughout the trip."

Of the *Starbound*, Kenneth Whitteker said: "She is free from the rolling and pitching that one often encounters on small sailing craft and is comfortable under all conditions."

Captain Culler wrote about his copy: "*Spray*'s motion was

200

quite easy, and although at times she seemed to jump around a lot, she seldom threw anything around below, or what is more surprising, off the table. She was really a very easy ship and not at all tiring. I'll take her model any time for motion you can work with."

The *Pandora* also had an easy motion, according to T. A. Dickson: "About 10 p.m. wind came up fresh W. St. Kilda, from this quarter, is a horribly exposed hole; many a night I have spent here under similar weather conditions, and the pitch and tumble of the ordinary yacht is very trying, but on *Pandora* there was a distinctly easy roll, and an entire absence of the ordinary rattle and bang which adds to, and indeed forms, the prevailing discomfort on a small yacht in a fresh breeze on a lee shore." [100]

Neal Small said of the *Sagamore* that the motion was "very comfortable. I don't remember a pot ever being tossed off the stove. The foredeck even is reasonable."

Henry Longmore wrote: "The lake waves are inclined to be short, giving a rather violent motion, but *Spray* took them very comfortably."

Herr Leisegang was satisfied with the *Heimat*, stating that she was easy in a sea.

Charles Hinman was not so enthusiastic about his *Ulula*. "Strangers coming aboard for the first time used to find her an awful 'sick maker,' as she was never quite still, even in the enclosed water of a dock. At sea, her great buoyancy made her very lively though she was not often violent. . . . With a fair wind she had a gentle roll. In a calm and a big sea she rolled madly, which is only to be expected."

Slocum also met his share of trying conditions. Sailing down the River Plate from Buenos Aires, a gale came up and caused an ugly sea. "The Plate is a treacherous place for storms. One sailing there should always be on the alert for squalls. I cast anchor before dark in the best lee I could find near the land, but was tossed miserably all night, heartsore of choppy seas." [101]

The *Spray* also suffered off the Cape of Good Hope, which

201

was living up to its reputation as the "Cape of Storms" with frequent gales and rough seas:

The *Spray* was trying to stand on her head, and she gave me every reason to believe that she would accomplish the feat before night. She began very early in the morning to pitch and toss about in a most unusual manner, and I have to record that, while I was at the end of the bowsprit reefing the jib, she ducked me under water three times for a Christmas box. I got wet and did not like it a bit: never in any other sea was I put under more than once in the same short space of time, say three minutes. A large English steamer passing ran up the signal "Wishing you a Merry Christmas." I think the captain was a humorist; his own ship was throwing her propeller out of water.[102]

Homeward bound, and in the midst of the turbulent Gulf Stream, the *Spray* also got shaken up. "She was jumping like a porpoise over the uneasy waves. As if to make up for lost time, she seemed to touch only the high places." [103]

Roger Strout also mentions being thrown about at times. "*Igdrasil* behaves very well in heavy seas in the open ocean, but shallow water is something quite different." [104] Elsewhere, he records heading south from Sandy Hook, when the *Igdrasil* met a southeast gale and had to beat into Delaware breakwater. "Under double reefs and with wind against tide, *Igdrasil* threw a third of her keel out of the water on every sea while making the last two miles." [105]

Gilbert Klingel's comment on his *Basilisk* just about sums up the position for the *Spray* type: "*Basilisk* did not roll particularly badly and in the open ocean was generally fairly comfortable. She was at her worst in restricted water when the seas were short and steep."

WATER ABOARD

Because of her stiffness and her buoyancy, the *Spray* was normally a dry sailer. Slocum commented on her dryness even when hove-to in heavy weather:

One particularly severe gale encountered near New Caledonia foundered the American clipper ship *Patrician* farther south. Again, nearer the coast of Australia, when, however, I was not aware that the gale was extraordinary, a French mail-steamer from New Caledonia for Sydney, blown considerably out of her course, on her arrival reported it an awful storm, and to inquiring friends said: "Oh, my! we don't know what has become of the little sloop *Spray*. We saw her in the thick of the storm." The *Spray* was all right, lying to like a duck. She was under a goose's wing mainsail, and had a dry deck while the passengers on the steamer, I heard later, were up to their knees in water in the saloon.[106]

Incidentally, a goose's wing mainsail was the name given to the gaff sail with its tack triced up. It was a method of reefing which was common enough in former days when the gaff rig held sway, but is now confined almost entirely to some fishing smacks which often do it when trawling.

Harold Smith recalled his sail with Slocum. "The usual strong summer southwesterly was blowing and under these conditions (Buzzard's Bay being open to the southwest) a rather nasty sea arises, and I was amazed at the ability of the *Spray* to sail easily under these conditions. She was dry in a seaway in which the average small yacht would have been burying herself."

Another gentleman who also sailed on the *Spray* was the well-known naval architect L. Francis Herreshoff. In *The Common Sense of Yacht Design* he had a different comment to make. "The full bows like *Spray*, Captain Slocum's yawl, are terrible. I have sailed on her a short way with the fine old gentleman. *Spray* was well named; she would spit spray all over you even in a light breeze and a small sea if close hauled. . . ."[107]

A couple of owners of copies noted some occasional spray, but, after all, what boat is immune from that? Charles Hinman said: "In a short sea she would sometimes bump into them and send aft a big shower of spray, but going to windward I only once saw her put her head in. After that I took out about seven hundredweight of ballast from under her fore-castle floors and put it in again under the engine. That cured her."

Otto Erdmann wrote of the Rochester *Spray:* "Even in very heavy weather no green water ever came aboard, although the

203

fore deck will be kept wet by the bluffness of the bow." [108] The owner, Herr Leisegang, added in a letter: "We hardly ever experienced water on deck; when we tacked across a short, rough sea, the water on deck was slight. I cannot remember that we ever took green water aboard. One can therefore rightly say that she was a dry ship, in spite of being what I consider over-ballasted. . . ."

About his *Sirius*, Bob Carr said: "I've had her before some pretty good gales but she's never shipped a sea over her stern even when running fast. Occasionally when driven into a head sea she'll take some solid water forward but never yet in any serious amount."

Neal Small commented: "*Sagamore* never sails along with a deck load of water. The best sailing I've experienced close hauled on *Sagamore* was crossing the Gulf Stream from Great Isaacs. The wind was just about the maximum for all sail— I don't remember more than a few slops of water on deck."

"About the only way to get water on the deck is with a bucket or a hose!" wrote Kenneth Whitteker of his *Starbound*.

Captain Culler stated: "*Spray* almost never took heavy water aboard."

Roger Strout said of the *Igdrasil:* "The beam is carried well into the ends to give the buoyancy that is required if you are to have a dry deck. A yacht with her lee rail submerged in a smother of foam makes a beautiful picture and may give a thrill of speed and adventure when experienced once a week. But as a steady diet it must be a frightful bore. Personally, I think the water looks much better over the side than slopping round on deck and the broad beam and short ends keep it there, most of the time at least." [109] In a letter he added: "Normally the only water on deck came through the scuppers."

Of course, there are times when even the best boat could not be expected to remain dry—in confused or broken seas and in storms, for example. Slocum wrote:

I remained at the helm, humoring my vessel in the cross seas, for it was rough, and I did not dare to let her take a straight course. It was necessary to change her course in the combing seas, to meet them with what skill I could when they rolled ahead, and to keep off when they came up abeam. . . .

Occasionally an old southwest sea, rolling up, combed athwart her, but did no harm. . . .

One wave, in the evening, larger than others that had threatened all day,—one such as sailors call "fine-weather seas,"—broke over the sloop fore and aft. It washed over me at the helm, the last that swept over the *Spray* off Cape Horn.[110]

After leaving the Cocos, Slocum wrote: "The sea was rugged, and the *Spray* washed heavily when hauled on the wind . . . which brought the sea abeam. . . . I naturally tired of the never-ending motion of the sea, and, above all, of the wetting I got whenever I showed myself on deck." [111]

In the southeast trades, after leaving Cape Town the *Spray* met a short, heaving sea. "She ran along steadily at her best speed . . . when suddenly a comber rolled over the stern and slopped saucily into the cabin, wetting the very book I was reading. Evidently it was time to put in a reef, that she might not wallow on her course." [112]

Roger Strout also had a note on short seas. "The reader must not think the Barrier Route is always smooth. Ocean swells are absent, it is true, but the short, steep, shallow water seas are the meanest things imaginable for a small boat. We even took one sea over the stern, the only one to board us from that direction in the whole voyage!" [113]

The *Basilisk* had a very bad time of it on her voyage. Gilbert Klingel said: *"Basilisk* was quite dry under ordinary sailing conditions, but most of my sailing on her was under severe conditions of storm and there were times when she had so much water over her that I wondered if she would ever come up."

ACCOMMODATION

It has often been stated that a hull of the *Spray* type is too shallow to offer any good accommodation. This would naturally be so without the use of trunk cabins; however, with the trend towards streamlined complexity in yachts, these have gone out of fashion, and are even apt to be condemned as unsafe for extended cruising! John Hanna put forward his views in *Motor Boat:*

The trunk has been so unmercifully and unjustly damned, by assertion and bluster and without logic or proof, that I am afraid it will be necessary for me to speak very plainly in discussing this point. In the lurid sea tales in the fiction magazines, from which most yachtsmen and yacht designers get their sea-going knowledge, the ship invariably has her deck houses swept off. But the tens of thousands of good ships that live long and useful careers with never a deck house lost, never get into print. Charles Mower, who took off *Spray's* lines, reports that while her hull and decks were tremendously heavy, the deck houses were light and flimsy. He believes that her loss was due to these weak and long battered structures finally giving way. I think it is quite probable, and if so, this one fact alone is positive proof of the absolute safety of the trunk cabin. For if such flimsy boxes could stand all the battering of all the storms on all the oceans traversed in that 46,000-mile voyage before they finally gave way, it is reasonably evident that strongly designed trunks, easily ten times as strong, would be good for nearly half a million miles, which would certainly seem to be enough to satisfy the most timid, don't you think? . . . It is quite all right to use a flush deck if one prefers its lack of light and ventilation and its dangerous glass-topped skylights, but it won't do to claim it the *only* safe and seaworthy type.[114]

The *Spray* was roomy, more so in fact than most boats her length. She was a vessel for solid comfort—a veritable floating home. Clifton Johnson, the father of Irving Johnson, former owner of the famous brigantine *Yankee*, visited the *Spray* after her long voyage, and wrote: "The *Spray*, as I first saw her, lay gently rocking in a little cove on the Massachusetts coast near Woods Hole. . . . There were other vessels about. . . . The *Spray* could not compete with them in grace and style, yet she had an attractive air of domesticity and was evidently built for a sea home suited to all seasons and all waters and not simply adapted to fair summer weather along shore. It was a pleasure to set foot on her and note her snug appointments." [115]

One incident recorded in Slocum's book illustrates the exceptional amount of room on this old vessel. At Samoa, Slocum was given a great reception. He could not, of course, entertain on the *Spray* in return, but welcomed as many visitors aboard as liked to come. Once the *Spray* had quite an unusual deck cargo. "One day the head teachers of Papauta College, Miss Schultze and Miss Moore, came on board with their ninety-seven young women students. They were all dressed in white, and each wore a red rose, and of course came in boats or canoes in the cold-climate style. A merrier bevy of girls it would be difficult to find. As soon as they got on deck, by request of one of the teachers, they sang 'The Watch on the Rhine,' which I had never heard before." [116] One hundred people aboard a 37 footer must be considered a fair number!

The spaciousness of the *Spray* was a feature much praised by owners of copies. Mrs. Culler said:

In order to take advantage of all possible space the *Spray* has no cockpit and the auxiliary is placed in the forepeak. This gives us a good-sized after cabin with two bunks and a table capable of seating six. The galley and toilet rooms are amidships. Then there is a large double stateroom with two bunks 36 inches wide and 5½ by 6 feet of floor space. The forepeak, having a separate house and hatch, contains the motor, boxed in to form a table, two bunks, headroom in spots to enable us to stand up to get our pants on, and another toilet room. There is full headroom throughout the after cabins and 12-inch ports which are a joy both for light and air and a means of seeing what's going on when you're below. [117]

Hubert Canfield, who did a three-week charter cruise on this *Spray*, was very enthusiastic about her roominess: "The *Spray* offers everything that a small boat can in the way of roominess below. It might seem like exaggeration, but many yachts twice her length are not as comfortable. . . . Let the Editor of Y.M. sail her for a day under such conditions, and spend the night in quarters actually ample for the life and ease of four or five people. After that the word 'tub' will be a word of endearment, for the *Spray* is both liveable and lovable." [118]

Charles Hinman commented on the *Ulula:* "On one occasion I entertained three R.A.F. officers and their wives on board. After dinner we put the cabin table in the forecastle and had room to dance! Not much room, but enough. . . . Her side decks were so wide that we could carry two nine-foot dinghies one each side turned up between the bulwarks and half lying on the cabin top."

Roger Strout wrote that the *Igdrasil* "is comfortable to live on, which is important when one lives aboard continuously." [119] He said further:

Sometimes the comments about her shape are a bit rank. I had just told a visitor that she was 37 feet long and 14 feet wide when he asked me which way I sailed her! The guest who compared the the area of our deck with a back block sheep station was, perhaps, a bit over-enthusiastic, but there is plenty of room for several ordinary canvas deck chairs. What is more important, we actually use such a chair when keeping wheel watch in all reasonable weather. Bulwarks extend the full length of the vessel and contribute much to the safety and peace of mind of those aboard. They will also keep anchors, cable and coils of halliards from washing overboard in heavy weather if they happen to get adrift. The usual cockpit and open deck complex is entirely lacking and one may stroll about the deck without a thought of holding on, even when under sail.[120]

CARRYING CAPACITY

In ocean cruising, there is another factor which is just as important for the small boat as living space, and that is storage space. The fine, clean lines of most modern craft usually deny them both.

Roger Strout summed up the position in *Yachting:*

. . . carrying capacity is denied the small yacht, almost by definition. Her designer calculated her weights and ballasted her to a hair. She is in sailing trim when the crew come aboard with their suitcases, or sea bags if they want to look tough, but if they bring their trunks the boat will be overloaded! This is, of course, quite right and proper on the small yacht designed for week-end and coastwise work or a race to Bermuda, but the long hauls are a different story.

Both economy and safety dictate that supplies for a year or more should be carried out of Panama. For two people on a 35- to 40-foot boat, this means some five tons, and the crew, with the assistance of the engine, eat her out of the water as they cross the Pacific. What, then, of the little yacht? Dangerously over-loaded and logy at the start, or light and cranky at the finish? I suppose any good naval architect can design a craft tolerant of loading, one that will sail safely though her displacement be varied over 30 or 40 per cent. But you cannot take the standard yacht design, with fixed ballast, and do this with impunity.[121]

One needs only to look at the *Spray*'s great beam to appreciate her ample capacity, either for people or stores. Slocum records taking on board a cord of firewood (128 cubic feet) in the Strait of Magellan, and Strout loaded the *Igdrasil* with half a cord of wood in Alaska. I wonder how many 37-footers, midway through a cruise, could take on such quantities if and when they wanted to.

Of *Igdrasil*'s carrying capacity, Roger Strout said:

If you cruise on a limited budget, you do some funny things, you buy things in quantity where they are best and cheapest. For example, a quarter of a ton, over two years' supply, of evaporated milk from the States and 425 gallons of petrol from the Panama Canal Zone, at ten cents a gallon! We had a paint-testing agreement with one of the big paint manufacturers who sent us half a ton of his product for trials in the tropics. This sort of thing may explain the small amount of ballast. We had a wood-burning stove and took scrap from the building yard to fuel it. After three years and 700 pounds of flour used in baking we still had about a third of our firewood left! *Igdrasil* was a capricious freighter.

RETROSPECT

We have gone into the performance of the *Spray* at length, and, point by point, considered what she and her copies have done. All the evidence available from those most qualified to know has been presented; now let us see what they thought of the boat in general.

Captain Joshua Slocum, who took the *Spray* around the world alone, said: "As a sailor judges his prospective ship by a 'blow of the eye' when he takes interest enough to look her over at all, so I judged the *Spray*, and I was not deceived. . . . I may some day see reason to modify the model of the dear old *Spray*, but out of my limited experience I strongly recommend her wholesome lines over those of pleasure-fliers for safety." [1]

Kenneth Whitteker, of the *Starbound*, in which he cruised for seven years on the eastern seaboard of the United States, said: "*Spray* has a rugged functional beauty that may not appeal to the modern yachtsman, but I am no longer young and I seek comfort of both body and mind. These I found in the *Spray*; it is the kind of boat that I like and to hell with what

210

others think or say. I will soon be building another using the exact dimensions of *Spray* rather than an enlarged version."

Captain Pete Culler, of the Oxford *Spray*, on which he and his wife lived for twenty-three years, cruising widely on the whole eastern coast of the United States, wrote: "She is all that has been said of her—safe, able, and fast for ocean work. However, a lot of this is misunderstood now as most people are concerned with these modern, chrome-plated ocean racers —good, no doubt, for their purpose, but evolved by style, social standards, and rating rules, not by usefulness for a home and general seafaring. The *Spray* type is out of place in what is called present-day thinking, though it effects the qualities of such a vessel not one bit. The design is not perfect, no boat ever is, but it's about as near as one will get."

Gilbert Klingel, of the *Basilisk*, in which he went through one of the severest winter storms the North Atlantic has seen, wrote: "I think there is no finer sea boat in the world for a small crew than *Spray*. There are very few designs which combine her performance and comfort with her size. I have always wanted another *Spray* and now intend to have one."

Roger Strout, of *Igdrasil*, in which he and his wife sailed around the world and later to Alaska, wrote: "I honestly believe that she was the safest and most comfortable vessel of her length that was ever built," he wrote in a letter. In *Yachting* he said: "Those who do their yachting according to Hoyle may disagree with me on many points and I shall not argue with them. I can only say that in *Igdrasil* I have voyaged in safety, eaten well, and slept in peace." [2]

Such were the words of men who, in their own reproductions of the *Spray*, found satisfaction and contentment. For them, Captain Joshua Slocum's immortal narrative was a source of inspiration and wisdom. As to whether their faith was justified, well—I hope the previous pages speak for themselves.

EPILOGUE

Those who find their dream ship in some sleek-bodied thorough-bred from an architect's drawing board will not see much in the stocky old *Spray*—so much a boat of chance, from her very design to her discovery by Slocum. But what matter if her lines are empirical; they are nonetheless worthy for that, rather all the more interesting because of it. Her form was the result of human trial and error, of hard toil and sweat down through the ages, of the endless endeavor of man against the sea—a product of the simple lives of simple people, with roots stretching far back into the mists of Time. How much more satisfying this, than that mathematically exact form which is coldly and deliberately planned at an office desk!

The *Spray* was no fashion piece. No refinement of hull or rig entered into her make-up; hers was the simple, rugged functionality of a fishing vessel—everything plain and businesslike. Yet, let her be judged, not merely as a "graceless drogher," but as an oceangoing vessel, whose sea-keeping qualities were proven on many a long passage. To many sailors of the present day, her model is still considered the most seaworthy and comfortable for extended voyages at sea.

But, yachtsmen, beware! Do not expect too much of the *Spray*. She is, first and foremost, a vessel to keep the sea, and her qualities inherent for that purpose handicap her severely in those conditions generally encountered in pleasure sailing. Slow, clumsy, and unhandy beside the modern yacht—to sail such a craft amid the congested harbors and steamer-ridden shores of these modern days requires a degree of skill far greater than the usual owner possesses. After all, there are few of us able to measure up to the standard of Captain Slocum. So, if you fancy building the *Spray*, look to your seamanship. In any case, be sensible, and install an engine—to compensate for her deficiencies, and to help you keep your dream ship longer.

And the *Spray* sails still—kept afloat in its continued reincarnation by yachtsmen; old copies and new, but worthy vessels all, fit to take their place on the oceans of the world as others of their kind have done. A great tribute to the past, this, and no finer expression of belief in the words of the old captain. Were he to return today, he would surely look with pride on the growing fleet of replicas of the little boat he loved so well.

To owners of all the copies of this grand old vessel, past and present—yes, and future, too—let us say "Well done!" and wish good luck and Godspeed, as they put to sea and sail in the wake of the *Spray*.

NOTES

INTRODUCTION

1. Captain Joshua Slocum, *Sailing Alone Around the World,* in Walter Magnes Teller, ed., *The Voyages of Joshua Slocum* (New Brunswick, N. J.: Rutgers University Press, 1958), pp. 375–76.

CHAPTER 2

1. London: Pan Books, Ltd., 1950, p. 5.
2. *Sailing Alone,* p. 231.
3. *Daily Telegraph* (London), September 8, 1900.
4. *Rudder,* January 1911, p. 62.

CHAPTER 3

1. *Sailing Alone,* p. 227.
2. *Ibid.,* p. 229.
3. *Ibid.,* p. 230.
4. *Ibid.,* p. 244.
5. *Ibid.,* p. 248.
6. *Ibid.,* p. 269.
7. *Ibid.,* p. 270.
8. *Ibid.,* p. 278.
9. *Ibid.,* pp. 293–94.

10. *Ibid.*, p. 299.
11. *Ibid.*, p. 306.
12. *Ibid.*, p. 332.
13. *Ibid.*, p. 353.
14. *Ibid.*, p. 369.

CHAPTER 4

1. *Sailing Alone*, p. 381.

CHAPTER 5

1. *Sailing Alone*, p. 379.

CHAPTER 6

1. Arthur Ransome, *Racundra's First Cruise* (London: Jonathan Cape, 1949), p. 17.
2. London: Rupert Hart-Davis, 1951, p. 319.
3. Victor Slocum, *Capt. Joshua Slocum: The Life and Voyages of America's Best Known Sailor* (New York: Sheridan House, 1950), p. 342.
4. London: Rupert Hart-Davis, 1954, p. 98.

CHAPTER 7

1. *Sailing Alone*, p. 374.
2. *Capt. Joshua Slocum*, p. 280.
3. New York: W. W. Norton & Company, 1951, pp. 244–45, 249–50, 252.
4. *Yachting Monthly*, April 1959, pp. 203–04.
5. *Ibid.*, December 1928, pp. 136–37.
6. *Rudder*, March 1957, p. 37.
7. *Capt. Joshua Slocum*, p. 274.

CHAPTER 8

1. *Sailing Alone*, p. 375.
2. January 1911, p. 62.
3. June 1950, p. 151.
4. April 1939, p. 489.

CHAPTER 9

1. July 1918, p. 185.
2. March 1957, p. 38.
3. London: Rupert Hart-Davis, 1955, p. 116.
4. *Sailing Alone*, p. 312.
5. *Ibid.*, pp. 312–13.

CHAPTER 10

1. *Capt. Joshua Slocum,* p. 279.
2. *Ibid.*
3. *Sailing Alone,* p. 236.
4. *Ibid.,* p. 332.
5. *Ibid.,* p. 258.
6. *Ibid.,* p. 265.
7. *Ibid.,* p. 290.
8. Walter Magnes Teller, *The Search for Captain Slocum* (New York: Charles Scribner's Sons, 1956), pp. 162–63.

CHAPTER 11

1. *Rudder,* January 1911, p. 62.
2. *Capt. Joshua Slocum,* p. 369.
3. *Ibid.,* p. 270.
4. *Motor Boat,* June 10, 1923, p. 17.
5. July 1950, p. 54.
6. January 1911, p. 62.
7. *Sailing Alone,* p. 228.
8. *Ibid.,* pp. 234–35.
9. *Ibid.,* pp. 235–36.
10. *Ibid.,* p. 276.
11. *Ibid.,* p. 319.
12. *Ibid.,* p. 370.
13. *Ibid.,* p. 372.
14. *Yachting Monthly,* April 1918, p. 386.
15. *The Search for Captain Slocum,* p. 229.
16. *Ibid.,* p. 230.
17. *The Voyages of Joshua Slocum,* p. 25.
18. *Rudder,* June 1912, p. 398.
19. *Capt. Joshua Slocum,* pp. 369–70.
20. *Sailing Alone,* p. 232.
21. *Ibid.,* p. 236.
22. *Ibid.,* p. 272.
23. *Ibid.,* p. 302.
24. September 1917, p. 307.

CHAPTER 12

1. *Sailing Alone,* p. 226.
2. *Ibid.,* p. 383.
3. *The Search for Captain Slocum,* p. 65.
4. *Capt. Joshua Slocum,* p. 370.

CHAPTER 13

1. February 1918, p. 251.
2. March 1918, p. 320.
3. December 1928, p. 137.
4. February 1929, p. 297.
5. *Yachting and Motor Boat Annual,* Season 1908–09, Perth, Western Australia.
6. *The Argus* (Melbourne), June 1, 1910.
7. *Capt. Joshua Slocum,* p. 274.
8. December 1927, pp. 31–32.
9. June 1926, p. 38.
10. *Ibid.,* pp. 38–39.
11. September 1926, pp. 28–30.
12. Pp. 30–31.
13. March 1951, p. 17.
14. June 10, 1923, pp. 13–14, 16.
15. April 1940, p. 22.
16. January–February 1931, p. 100.
17. New York: Dodd, Mead & Company, pp. 6–9.
18. September 1937, pp. 52–53.
19. *The Spray,* May 1957, p. 70.
20. January 1951, p. 101.
21. *Rudder,* October 1946, p. 25.
22. July 1954, pp. 27, 104.
23. November 1959, p. 26.
24. London: Methuen, 1944, p. 168.

CHAPTER 14

1. *Boston Herald,* April 16, 1895.
2. *Boston Globe,* April 16, 1895.
3. *Sailing Alone,* pp. 237–38.
4. *Ibid.,* p. 239.
5. *Ibid.,* pp. 243, 245.
6. *Ibid.,* p. 253.
7. *Ibid.,* pp. 299–300.
8. *Ibid.,* p. 335.
9. *Ibid.,* pp. 355–56.
10. *Ibid.,* pp. 376, 379.
11. *Ibid.,* p. 376.
12. *The New York Times,* November 7, 1899.
13. *Sailing Alone,* pp. 374, 379.
14. July 1917, p. 186.
15. August 1917, p. 244.
16. September 1917, p. 30.

17. October 1917, p. 376.
18. November 1917, p. 49.
19. April 1918, p. 385.
20. *Ibid.*
21. *Sailing Alone*, pp. 263–64.
22. *Ibid.*, p. 264.
23. *The Search for Captain Slocum*, p. 226.
24. London: Putnam & Company, 1952, p. 92.
25. April 1940, p. 56.
26. P. 30.
27. *Sailing Alone*, p. 376.
28. April 1940, p. 23.
29. February 1911, p. 106.
30. August 1911, p. 58.
31. London: Robert Ross & Company, 1949, p. 62.
32. *Motor Boat*, June 10, 1923, p. 16.
33. September 1937, p. 108.
34. December 1937, p. 34.
35. *Sailing Alone*, pp. 376, 379.
36. *Ibid.*, p. 231.
37. *Ibid.*, p. 250.
38. December 1928, p. 137.
39. London: Edward Arnold, Ltd., 1933, p. 95.
40. *Motor Boat*, June 10, 1923, p. 14.
41. *The Spray*, April 1957, p. 62.
42. London: Oxford University Press, 1950, p. 10.
43. *Sailing Alone*, p. 268.
44. *Cruising Under Sail*, p. 10.
45. May 1940, p. 51.
46. August 1911, pp. 57–58.
47. *Once Is Enough* (London: Rupert Hart-Davis, 1959), p. 198.
48. P. 290.
49. March 1938, p. 42.
50. June 1938, p. 44.
51. *Capt. Joshua Slocum*, pp. 238–39.
52. *Sailing Alone*, p. 226.
53. *Ibid.*, p. 267.
54. Volume X, April 9, 1896, p. 344.
55. *Boston Globe*, April 16, 1895.
56. *Capt. Joshua Slocum*, p. 301.
57. *Sailing Alone*, p. 234.
58. *Ibid.*, p. 370.
59. August 1911, p. 57.
60. *Yachting*, January 1938, p. 224.
61. *Sailing Alone*, p. 275.

62. *The Sydney Daily Telegraph,* October 6, 1896.
63. *Yachting,* June 1938, pp. 44–45.
64. *Yachting Monthly,* February 1939, p. 277.
65. *Rudder,* August 1911, pp. 56–57.
66. *Sailing Alone,* p. 280.
67. *The Search for Captain Slocum,* p. 201.
68. *Rudder,* April 1940, p. 23.
69. *Yachting,* September 1937, p. 53.
70. *Sailing Alone,* pp. 237, 239.
71. *Ibid.,* p. 311.
72. March 1938, p. 43.
73. *Sailing Alone,* pp. 239–40.
74. November 1928, p. 60.
75. August 1953, p. 30.
76. *Sailing Alone,* p. 321.
77. April 1940, p. 56.
78. *Sailing Alone,* p. 246.
79. *The Search for Captain Slocum,* p. 69.
80. *Sailing Alone,* p. 326.
81. *Ibid.,* p. 347.
82. *Ibid.,* p. 348.
83. *Boston Globe,* April 16, 1895.
84. *The Search for Captain Slocum,* p. 81.
85. *Rudder,* April 1940, p. 56.
86. London: Seeley, Service & Company, 1948, p. 514.
87. *Rudder,* April 1940, p. 56.
88. *Capt. Joshua Slocum,* pp. 305–06.
89. *Sailing Alone,* p. 258.
90. *Ibid.,* p. 299.
91. *The Search for Captain Slocum,* p. 135.
92. *Rudder,* April 1940, p. 56.
93. *Yachting,* September 1937, p. 54.
94. *Rudder,* April 1940, p. 23.
95. *Motor Boat,* June 10, 1923, p. 16.
96. *Sailing Alone,* p. 251.
97. *Ibid.,* p. 252.
98. *Ibid.,* pp. 355–56.
99. *Yachting Monthly,* April 1918, p. 385.
100. *Rudder,* February 1911, p. 106.
101. *Sailing Alone,* p. 266.
102. *Ibid.,* pp. 351–52.
103. *Ibid.,* p. 369.
104. *Yachting,* February 1938, p. 116.
105. *Yachting Monthly,* February 1939, p. 271.
106. *Sailing Alone,* p. 311.

107. New York: Rudder Publishing Company, 1947, Vol. I, p. 11.
108. *Yachting Monthly*, February 1929, p. 297.
109. *Yachting*, September 1937, pp. 54, 107.
110. *Sailing Alone*, p. 293.
111. *Ibid.*, p. 340.
112. *Ibid.*, p. 355.
113. *Yachting*, March 1938, p. 43.
114. June 10, 1923, p. 17.
115. *The Search for Captain Slocum*, p. 192.
116. *Sailing Alone*, p. 308.
117. *Rudder*, April 1940, p. 23.
118. *Yachting Monthly*, February 1939, p. 340.
119. *Ibid.*, April 1937, p. 477.
120. *Yachting*, September 1937, p. 107.
121. *Ibid.*, p. 52.

CHAPTER 15

1. *Sailing Alone*, pp. 376, 383.
2. November 1937, p. 113.

APPENDIX I:
ANALYSIS TABLES AND FIGURES

TABLE 1. Curve of Upright Areas

Station	Upright immersed areas		Ordinates (⅕ scale)	
Fore end LWL	0		0	
1	1.70 sq. ft.		0.34	
2	11.26 "		2.25	
3	18.42 "		3.68	
4	23.22 "		4.64	
5	25.92 "		5.18	
6	26.85 "		5.37	
7	25.58 "		5.12	
8	22.60 "		4.52	
9	17.90 "		3.58	
10	11.38 "		2.28	
11	* 0.38 sq. ft.	†Δ 0.82 sq. ft.	* 0.08	†Δ 0.16
Aft end LWL	* 0	†Δ 0.72 sq. ft.	* 0	†Δ 0.12
* Excluding rudder † Including rudder			Δ Rudder thickness assumed 3"	
Area curve upright areas			* 112.08 sq. ft.	† 112.20 sq. ft.
Correction for scale (×5) → displacement			* 560.40 cu. ft.	† 561.00 cu. ft.
Displacement			* 36,034 lb. (16.09 tons) † 36,072 lb. (16.10 tons)	

225

TABLE 2. Curve of Heeled Areas

Station	† Heeled immersed areas	Ordinates (⅕ scale)
Fore end LWL	0	0
1	1.82 sq. ft.	0.36
2	12.26 "	2.45
3	19.80 "	3.96
4	24.64 "	4.93
5	27.27 "	5.45
6	28.28 "	5.66
7	26.91 "	5.38
8	24.00 "	4.80
9	19.45 "	3.89
10	13.34 "	2.67
11	*Δ 1.55 "	0.31
Aft end LWL	Δ 0.72 "	0.12
* Including rudder Δ Rudder thickness 3″ assumed † Heeled to top of deck line (14.3°)		
Area curve heeled areas:		120.29 sq. ft.
Correction for scale (×5) → Displacement:		601.45 cu. ft.
Displacement (heeled):		38,673 lb.

226

TABLE 2A. Curve of Heeled Areas (Hull Rise 1½")

Station	Heeled immersed areas	Ordinates (⅕ scale)
Fore end LWL	0	0
1	1.46 sq. ft.	0.29
2	11.17 "	2.23
3	18.40 "	3.68
4	23.03 "	4.61
5	25.60 "	5.12
6	26.62 "	5.32
7	25.33 "	5.07
8	22.50 "	4.50
9	18.08 "	3.62
10	12.21 "	2.44
11	*Δ 1.49 "	0.30
Aft end LWL	Δ 0.73 "	0.15
* Including rudder Δ Rudder thickness 3" assumed		
Area curve heeled areas:	112.19 sq. ft.	
Correction for scale (×5) → Displacement:	560.95 cu. ft.	
Displacement:	36,069 lb.	
This displacement compares favorably to the upright displacement of 36,072 lb.		

227

TABLE 3. Vertical Displacement Curve

Water line	½ area WL plane	Ordinate (¹⁄₂₀ scale)
LWL	175.31 sq. ft.	8.76
½ B	166.17 "	8.31
1 B	156.53 "	7.83
1½ B	143.07 "	7.15
2 B	128.53 "	6.43
2½ B	111.12 "	5.56
3 B	93.80 "	4.69
3½ B	75.21 "	3.76
4 B	59.21 "	2.96
4½ B	41.91 "	2.09
5 B	27.67 "	1.38
5½ B	15.15 "	0.76
6 B	8.12 "	0.41
6½ B	5.70 "	0.28
7 B	4.15 "	0.21
7½ B	2.65 "	0.13
8 B	0.90 "	0.04
* 4-1-14 below LWL	0 "	0
½ Area vertical displacement curve:		14.07 sq. ft.
Area vertical displacement curve:		28.14 sq. ft.
Correction for scale (×20) → Displacement:		562.80 cu. ft.
Displacement:		36,019 lb.
Upright center of buoyancy is * 1-1-3 below LWL (determined by poising of paper cut-out) * Measurement in feet, inches, sixteenths.		

228

TABLE 4. Weight per Inch Immersion/Emersion at LWL

* Weight added	Distance	LWL raised Boat lowered
1,800 lb.	1 inch	
3,700 "	2 "	
5,650 "	3 "	
7,500 "	4 "	
9,480 "	5 "	
11,440 "	6 "	
* Weight subtracted	Distance	LWL lowered Boat raised
1,800 lb.	1 inch	
3,670 "	2 "	
5,370 "	3 "	
7,200 "	4 "	
9,000 "	5 "	
10,740 "	6 "	

* Values taken off graph (Fig. 3)

TABLE 5. Righting Moments on Heeling

Heel	* Righting lever	Righting moment	
		ft. lb.	ft. tons
10°	0-11-0	33,186	14.82
20°	1-5-10	53,026	23.67
30°	1-7-11	59,158	26.41
40°	1-7-5	58,076	25.84
50°	1-6-4	54,829	24.48
60°	1-4-15	50,862	22.71
70°	1-1-6	40,040	17.87
80°	0-8-6	25,250	11.27
90°	0-2-9	7,575	3.38
100°	−(0-3-6)	−10,100	−4.51

* Measurement in feet, inches, sixteenths.

TABLE 6. Upright Transverse Metacenter

Station	½ LWL widths	Cubes ½ LWL widths	Areas ½ upright sections
0	0	0	0
1	1.20 ft.	1.73	0.85 sq. ft.
2	4.06 "	66.90	5.63 "
3	5.63 "	162.80	9.21 "
4	6.42 "	264.90	11.61 "
5	6.81 "	316.30	12.96 "
6	6.93 "	333.10	13.42 "
7	6.80 "	314.60	12.79 "
8	6.49 "	273.60	11.30 "
9	6.03 "	219.20	8.95 "
10	5.28 "	147.40	5.69 "
11	3.80 "	54.80	0.44 "
Transom	3.50 "	42.82	0.25 "
Total:		2,198.15	93.10 "

U.T.M. is $\dfrac{2,198.15}{3 \times 93.10}$ ft. above U.C.B.

U.T.M. is 7.86 ft. above U.C.B.
  (* 7-10-5)
  therefore U.T.M. is * 6-9-2 above L.W.L.
* Measurement in feet, inches, sixteenths.

Note: The metacentric axis on body plan cuts WL 6B 2-6-0 from C.L.

TABLE 7. Metacentric Shelf and Curve of Moments

| Station | *Metacentric Shelf △ Distance from metacentric axis | | Curve of heeled area ordinates | †Curve of Moments | | | |
| | Windward | Leeward | | Discrepancy | | Product | |
				Windw.	Leew.	Windw.	Leew.
Fore end LWL	–	–	0	–	–	0	–
1	1.64 ft.	–	0.36	1.64'	–	0.59	–
2	0.94 "	–	2.45	0.94'	–	2.30	–
3	0.49 "	–	3.96	0.49'	–	1.94	–
4	0.24 "	–	4.93	0.24'	–	1.19	–
5	0.15 "	–	5.45	0.15'	–	0.82	–
6	0.13 "	–	5.66	0.13'	–	0.73	–
7	0.12 "	–	5.38	0.12'	–	0.64	–
8	0.15 "	–	4.80	0.15'	–	0.72	–
9	0.17 "	–	3.89	0.17'	–	0.66	–
10	0.17 "	–	2.67	0.17'	–	0.45	–
1-8-4 aft #10	φ 0.14 "	–	1.37	0.14'	–	0.19	–
2-0-8 aft #10	φ 0.06 "	–	1.00	0.06'	–	0.06	–
2-5-0 aft #10		φ 0.15 ft.	0.60	–	0.15'	–	0.09
2-8-8 aft #10		φ 0.22 "	0.40	–	0.22'	–	0.09
11		φ 0.34 "	0.31	–	0.34'	–	0.09
Aft end LWL	–	1.30 "	0.12	–	1.30'	–	0.16

* Heeled to #6 top of deck

φ Assuming sternpost 4" diameter, rudder 3" thick.

† For metacentric axis

△ Actual, not scale

TABLE 8. Prometacentric Shelf and Curve of Moments

| Station | *Prometacentric Shelf | | Curve of heeled area ordinates | †Curve of Moments | | | |
| | Δ Discrepancy | | | Discrepancy | | Product | |
	Windward	Leeward		Windw.	Leew.	Windw.	Leew.
Fore end LWL	—	—	0	—	—	0	—
1	1.39 ft.	—	0.36	1.39'	—	0.50	—
2	0.69 "	—	2.45	0.69'	—	1.69	—
3	0.24 "	—	3.96	0.24'	—	0.95	—
4	—	0.01 ft.	4.93	—	0.01'	—	0.05
5	—	0.10 "	5.45	—	0.10'	—	0.54
6	—	0.12 "	5.66	—	0.12'	—	0.68
7	—	0.13 "	5.38	—	0.13'	—	0.70
8	—	0.10 "	4.80	—	0.10'	—	0.48
9	—	0.08 "	3.89	—	0.08'	—	0.31
10	—	0.08 "	2.67	—	0.08'	—	0.21
1-8-4 aft #10	—	0.11 "	1.37	—	0.11'	—	0.15
2-0-8 aft #10	—	0.19 "	1.00	—	0.19'	—	0.19
2-5-0 aft #10	—	0.40 "	0.60	—	0.40'	—	0.24
2-8-8 aft #10	—	0.47 "	0.40	—	0.47'	—	0.19
11	—	0.59 "	0.31	—	0.59'	—	0.18
Aft end LWL	—	1.55 "	0.12	—	1.55'	—	0.19

* Prometacentric axis 0.25' to windward   † For prometacentric shelf   △ Actual, not scale
Note: The prometacentric axis on body plan cuts WL 6B 2-3-0 from CL
The prometacenter on body plan is 5-9-0 above LWL

TABLE 9. Sail Areas and Centers of Effort

Sail	Area	Center of effort			
Jib	249 sq. ft.	14-11-6 above LWL		2-0-10	aft #0
Main	612 "	20-2-5	"	20-10-12	"
Mizzen	151 "	15-3-1	"	40-10-0	"
Main+mizzen	763 "	19-2-9	"	24-10-2	"
Main+jib	861 "	18-7-13	"	15-4-15	"
Main+mizzen+ jib	1012 "	18-1-11	"	19-2-8	"
Note: Measurements in feet, inches, sixteenths. #0 is at the intersection of rabbit and deck lines.					

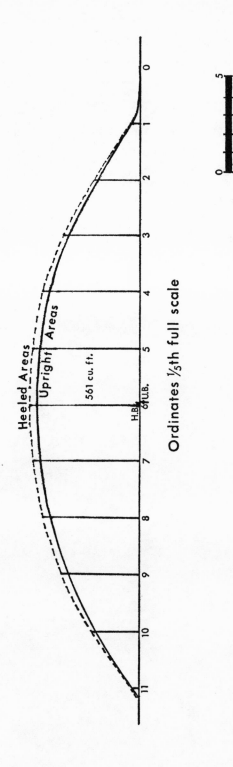

Ordinates 1/5th full scale

Fig. 1. Curve of Upright and Heeled Areas

234

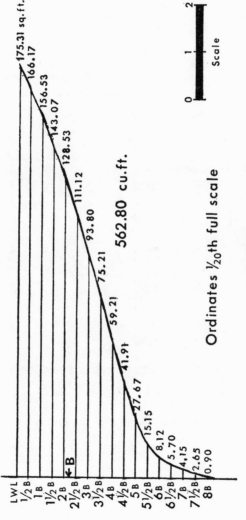

LWL
½B
1B
1½B
2B
2½B
3B
3½B
4B
4½B
5B
5½B
6B
6½B
7B
7½B
8B

175.31 sq.ft.
166.17
156.53
143.07
128.53
111.12
93.80
75.21
59.21
41.91
27.67
15.15
8.12
5.70
4.15
2.65
0.90

B

562.80 cu.ft.

Ordinates ¹⁄₂₀th full scale

0   1   2
Scale

Fɪɢ. 2. Vertical Displacement Curve

235

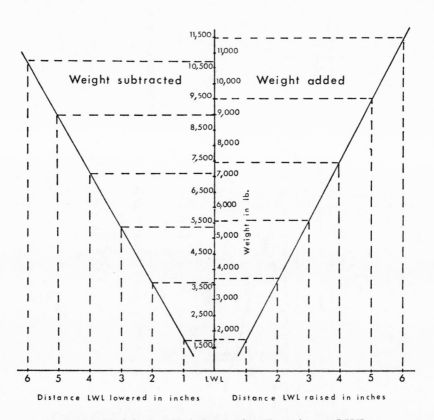

FIG. 3. Weight per Inch Immersion/Emersion at LWL

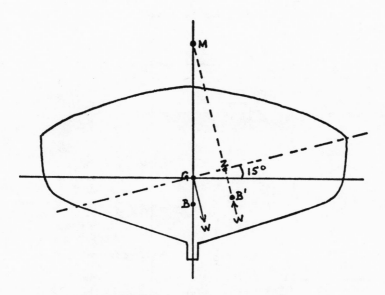

FIG. 4. Hull Values at Rest and Heeled

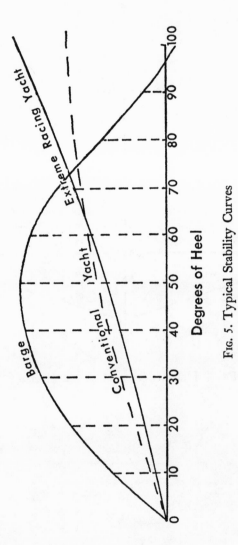

Fɪɢ. 5. Typical Stability Curves

Degrees of Heel

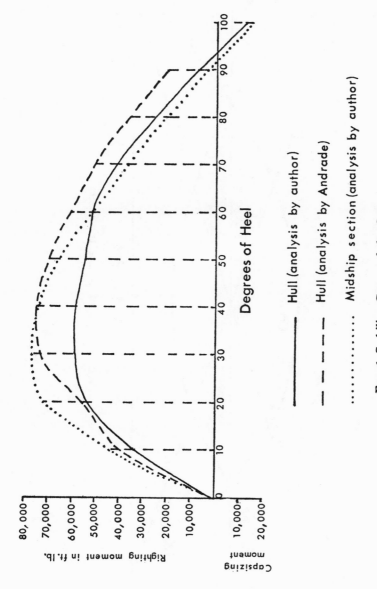

Fig. 6. Stability Curve of the *Spray*

—————— Hull (analysis by author)

— — — — Hull (analysis by Andrade)

· · · · · · · · · Midship section (analysis by author)

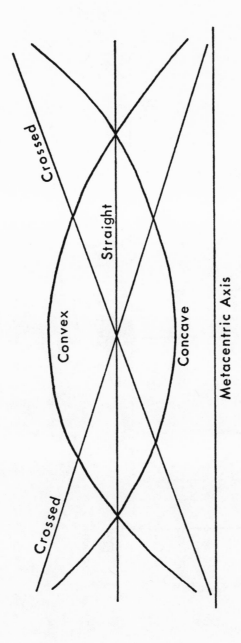

Fig. 7. Types of Metacentric Shelf

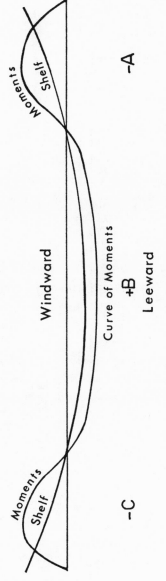

Fig. 8. Typical Shelf and Curve of Moments for a Symmetrical Hull

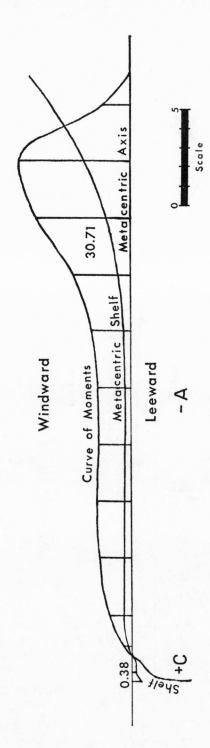

Fig. 9. Metacentric Shelf and Curve of Moments

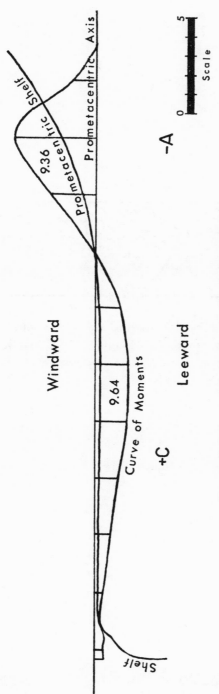

Fig. 10. Prometacentric Shelf and Curve of Moments

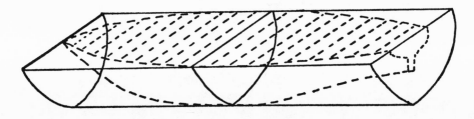

Volume enclosed by dotted line = displacement
Solid line indicates prism of length = L.W.L. length
          and cross section = max. W.L. cross section
Shaded area = L.W.L. plane

Fig. 11. The Prismatic Coefficient

APPENDIX II:
"A CRITICAL ANALYSIS
OF THE YAWL 'SPRAY'"
by Cipriano Andrade, Jr.

THE RUDDER

(June 1909)

A CRITICAL ANALYSIS
OF THE YAWL "SPRAY"

C. ANDRADE, JR.

"I did not know the center of effort in her sails, except as it hit me in practice at sea, nor did I care a rope yarn about it. Mathematical calculations, however, are all right in a good boat, and *Spray* could have stood them. She was easily balanced and easily kept in trim."

With these words Captain Joshua Slocum dismisses the technique of *Spray*'s design.

Considering the unparalleled performances of this little boat, it is remarkable that no one has ever attempted an analysis of her lines and sail plan.

Spray was built about the year 1800, and was used as an oysterman on the coast of Delaware. Her original lines were those of a North Sea fisherman. For almost a century she ranged up and down the Atlantic coast, and at length found her way to Fairhaven, at the head of Buzzards Bay. There she was finally hauled out, as everyone supposed, for her last rest.

In the year 1892, however, Captain Eben Pierce, her then owner, presented her to Captain Slocum. Slocum set to work with his own hands and rebuilt her from the keel up, so that not a particle of the original fabric remained, except the windlass, and the "fiddle head" or carving on the end of the cutwater. In rebuilding her, Slocum added to her freeboard 12 inches amidships, 18 inches forward and 14 inches aft. The lines published herewith show her as thus rebuilt.

Under a sloop rig, Slocum sailed *Spray* from New Bedford, Mass., to Gibraltar, thence back again across the Atlantic, down the South American coast and through the Strait of Magellan. Then he changed her rig to a yawl, and completed his circumnavigation of the globe by way of the Southern Pacific and Cape of Good Hope, and back across the Atlantic to New England—a gross of some 46,000 sea miles—all single-handed.

One of the most remarkable things about *Spray* is her ability to hold her course for hours or days at a time with no one at the

247

helm. Had she not possessed this quality, Slocum's performance would have been a physical impossibility. For example, she ran from Thursday Island to the Keeling Cocos Islands, 2,700 miles, in twenty-three days. Slocum stood at the helm for one hour during that time. Her average distance made good for the run was over 117

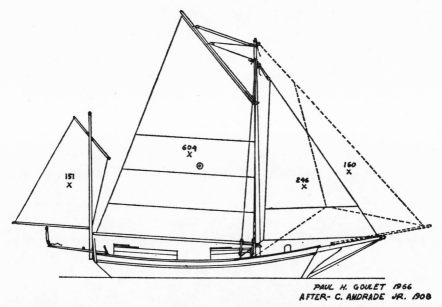

PAUL H. GOULET 1966
AFTER- C. ANDRADE JR. 1908

Sail Plan of "Spray"

miles a day or about 5 miles an hour. This was a fair cruising speed for *Spray*, and she maintained that speed of 5 knots for twenty-three consecutive days, or 552 consecutive hours. The impossibility of steering a boat for that time, or for any considerable portion of that time, is of course obvious. There are well-known men right here in New York City who have seen boats do the same thing for comparatively short distances. Thus, Mr. Day records that after he had converted *Sea-Bird* into a keel boat and had lengthened her keel, he laid her on a course and she held that course for an hour and a half, at the end of which time there came a change in the wind. Now if a boat will hold her course alone for an hour and a half, she will hold it for a year and a half, *provided always* that the wind and sea remain unchanged.

Examine an ocean chart of *Spray*'s voyage, and you will see that

248

Slocum systematically ran down the trades, not only for hundreds but for thousands of miles, and his wind and sea conditions for whole days and weeks must have been practically constant. This is one of the reasons for *Spray*'s phenomenal runs. Perfect balance is the other reason.

After a thorough analysis of *Spray*'s lines, I found her to have a theoretically perfect balance. Her balance is marvelous—almost uncanny. Try as I would—one element after the other—they all swung into the same identical line. I attacked her with proportional dividers, planimeter, rota-meter, Simpson's rule, Froude's coefficients, Dixon Kemp's formulae, series, curves, differentials, and all the appliances of modern yacht designing, and she emerged from the ordeal a theoretically perfect boat. For when she is underway, every element of resistance, stability, weight, heeling effort, and propulsive force is in one transverse plane, and that plane is the boat's midship section. I know of no similar case in the whole field of naval architecture, ancient or modern. There may be similar cases in existence, but it has not been my good fortune to know of them.

Before passing to a critical analysis of the figures, I shall take up a few general questions concerning this unusual boat.

GENERAL APPEARANCE

Spray's lines appear, in much reduced size, at the end of Slocum's book, "Sailing Alone Around the World." When I first looked at them, and read Slocum's statement that this hull had been driven at a speed of 8 knots, I thought he must be mistaken.

Slocum, however, is an accurate historian; and I therefore set to work with proportional dividers, and laid *Spray* out to a scale of ½ inch to the foot, in order to acquire an intimate personal knowledge of her lines—merely looking at them in a book will not always suffice. I next swept in two diagonals (*A* and *B* in the half-breadth plan), which are omitted from the lines as published in Slocum's book, and then I realized that he was justified in his claim of 8 knots.

DIAGONALS

If you will look at the drawings, you will see that *Spray*'s real working line is the diagonal *B*, which is a normal practically the whole length of the boat. On the half-breadth plan, you will see that diagonal *B* is marked by a little cross between stations 3 and 6.

At this point she takes the water. From the cross to station 6, there is a very coarse angle of entrance, of which I shall have more to say in a moment. From station 6 to the transom, a run of over 27 feet, diagonal B is as clean a line, as fine drawn, easy running and fair as you will find in any racer of the Larchmont fleet—and that is the line that bears her; it is the line she runs on, and it is the measure of her speed.

Now let us take up that coarse entrance angle of diagonal B from the cross to station 6—a matter of some two feet.

Twenty years ago, Mr. Herreshoff announced that hollow bow lines were not essential to speed.

The Whitehead torpedo, which travels at about 30 knots, has a nose as round as a cannon-ball.

Some of the little scow boats on the Western lakes develop great speed, and they hold this speed through rough water (that is, rough for their size and length), and their bows show hard curves, and in some cases even flat transoms.

Viewing all these things with impartial eyes, I should say that the two feet of diagonal B in *Spray* from the cross to section 6 would be no detriment whatever to her speed.

BOW

Let us now consider that portion of diagonal B which lies forward of the cross. This portion of the diagonal runs up to the stem-head at an angle somewhere in the neighborhood of 45°. The water-lines do the same and the buttock lines do the same. The result is a bow of terrific power. With her thirty-five thousand odd pounds of dead-weight and a few more thousand sail pressure on top of that, *Spray* can go coasting down the side of a roller, and then when she turns from the long down-grade up-hill again, instead of running under, or carrying a ton or so of water aft along her decks, that bow will lift her. And it is the only bow that would lift her.

STERN

Spray's stern is the best that my limited experience could suggest. There is just enough rake in her transom to lift her handsomely over any following sea. Her transom is broad enough and deep enough to hold her water-lines and buttocks easy to the very last moment. And the practice of dropping the bottom of her transom

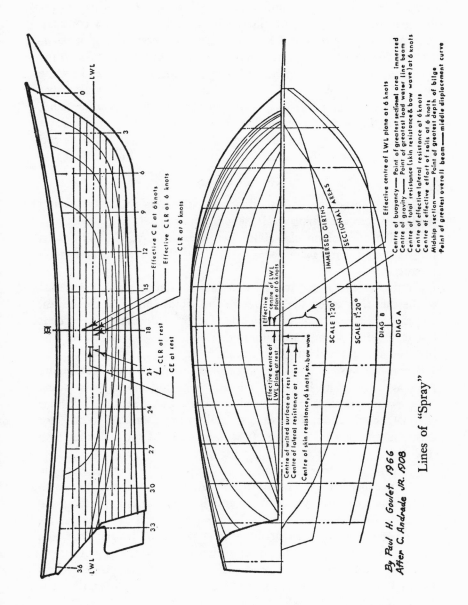

Centre of buoyancy——— Effective centre of LWL plane at 6 knots
Centre of gravity——— Point of greatest sectional area immersed
Centre of total resistance (skin resistance & bow wave) at 6 knots——— Point of greatest load water line beam
Centre of effective lateral resistance at 6 knots
Centre of effective effort of sails at 6 knots
Midship section——— Point of greatest depth of bilge
Point of greatest overall beam———middle displacement curve

IMMERSED GIRTHS

SECTIONAL AREAS

Effective centre of LWL plane at 6 knots

SCALE 1":20'

SCALE 1":20'

DIAG B

DIAG A

Effective centre of LWL plane at rest

Centre of wetted surface at rest
Centre of lateral resistance at rest
Centre of skin resistance,6 knots,ex, bow wave

LWL

0

3

6

9

12

15

18

21

24

27

30

33

36

LWL

Effective C E at 6knots

Effective CLR at 6 knots

CLR at 6 knots

CLR at rest

CE at rest

By Paul H. Goulet 1966
After C. Andrade JR. 1908

Lines of "Spray"

251

below the water-line finds support in such examples as Mr. Crane's *Dixie II* and Mr. Herreshoff's *Sea Shell*, and many other master designed craft. It does ease up the buttock lines so; and contrary to popular superstition, it does not create any material drag of dead-water. The Crosbys have been building catboats this way for years. By dropping the transom below the water-line, the water lifts the boat to the very end of the run, and one of the resultants of that lift on the buttock lines is a forward thrust. On the other hand, where the knuckle of the transom is above the water-line, the exact opposite takes place, and the water, instead of lifting the boat and thrusting her forward, is lifted by the boat and holds her back.

MIDSHIP SECTION

Spray's midsection, at first glance, would seem much wider and shallower than a seagoing model would require.

But like everything else about her, there is a very good reason for *Spray*'s form of midsection; in fact, there are several good reasons.

Firstly: I have heard it said, that her immunity from loss is due to the fact that when she is hove to she yields and gives to the sea, constantly easing away to leeward; whereas a deeper, more ardent model, holding in uncompromising fashion to the wind, would be battered and strained into destruction.

Secondly: *Spray*'s great breadth gives her no end of deck room. Now when you are living on a boat weeks and months and years, deck room becomes not only important, but essential. Without adequate deck room for walking and exercise, a man could not exist for that length of time. He would fall ill of some sickness and die.

Thirdly: The form of *Spray*'s midship section insures that she will never heel to an uncomfortable angle. She would rarely go down much below 10° of heel, and in good sailing breezes, she would probably not exceed 5°. Now equally with deck room, this matter of heel is most essential to the comfort and, in the long run, the health of the crew. The strain of living on a boat at 25 or 30° of heel may be borne for the brief period of a race, maybe a race as far as Bermuda. But when it comes to living on a boat thus for weeks at a time, no human being could stand it.

Fourthly: *Spray* is a much better boat to windward than her form of midsection would at first glance indicate. To the casual

252

TRANSVERSE METACENTERS, LOAD WATER-LINES AND CENTERS OF BUOYANCY YAWL "SPRAY"

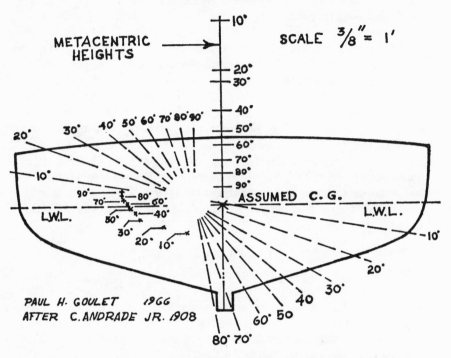

METACENTRIC HEIGHTS

SCALE $\frac{3}{8}'' = 1'$

ASSUMED C. G.

L.W.L.   L.W.L.

PAUL H. GOULET 1966
AFTER C. ANDRADE JR. 1908

observer, it would seem almost impossible to drive her to windward at all without a centerboard (and she has no centerboard). But on careful analysis it will appear that there are three reasons why *Spray* should be a fairly good boat to windward.

In the first place, she has an unusually hard bilge and an unusually flat vertical side, and the result is that even at a small angle of heel, her lee side acts as an efficient leeboard of very considerable area.

In the second place, she has a long, fairly deep keel, and as this keel rakes downward from the forefoot to the rudder, it is constantly entering solid water at every portion of its length, and is very much more efficient than if the keel were horizontal.

In the third place, *Spray* has a large lateral plane in proportion to her sail spread.

Therefore, like everything else about her, I should say that her form of midsection was fully justified.

253

DISPLACEMENT

For a boat of 32 feet water-line, *Spray*'s displacement is enormous—35,658 lb. Of course, this is an essential in her design. Being an oceangoing cruiser, her construction is heavy, 1½-inch yellow pine planking. Her great breadth requires heavy deck beams, 6 inch by 6-inch yellow pine; and her construction in other particulars is equally massive. All this means displacement. Then her crew, even one man, consumes a good deal of water, food and fuel in the course of several months. She must carry a large supply of spare gear and stores. Her large displacement then is necessary, unavoidable; and, besides, it gives her power to carry on through a sea.

By reason of her large water-line plane, her displacement per inch immersion at the load water-line is very large, 1,863 lb. This is a good feature, as it makes little difference in her trim whether she has a ton or so more or less of stores on board. This feature is still another advantage accruing from her wide shallow form of midship section.

CENTERS OF RESISTANCE, WEIGHT, ETC.

We now come to the inner mystery of *Spray*'s design.

I suppose that the extraordinary focusing of her centers is the result of chance. *Spray* was laid down about the year 1800. Analytic boat designing, as we understand it, was unknown at that time. *Spray*'s perfection of balance, then, must be purely empirical, but it is none the less marvelous for that.

To begin with, *Spray*'s center of buoyancy is located exactly at the boat's midship section. This is unusual. In fact, at the moment I do not recall any other design that has even this peculiarity. Axiomatically, the center of gravity and the center of buoyancy must lie in the same vertical line; and thus at the very outset of our investigations we find that the center of gravity, the center of buoyancy, the greatest breadth, the greatest depth of bilge, and the maximum point in the boat's curve of displacement, all fall exactly on the same line, which happens to be station 18.

And what is still more unusual, it will be observed that station 18, containing within itself all these elements, falls at exactly the effective middle point of the boat's curve of displacement. A glance at the curve of displacement will show that for all practical purposes the portion lying forward of station 3, and aft of station 33, can be disregarded. In other words, for all practical purposes, the curve begins at station 3 and ends at station 33, and exactly midway between station 3 and station 33 lies station 18, at which are focused all the points above-mentioned.

Let us now examine station 18 with reference to its position on the load water-line. The old school of designers who pinned their faith to the wave-line theory, held that the maximum point in the curve of displacement (station 18 in *Spray*) should be .60 of the L. W. L. aft from the forward point of immersion. Modern practice has discarded the coefficient .60, and says that it should be .55; and the measurement rule now in force adopts this coefficient of .55. *Spray*'s coefficient, however, instead of being .60 or .55, is only .506; which means that her midsection is somewhat forward of the position which has been decreed by modern practice.

Now, all displacement curves under the wave-line rule and under the modern practice show a marked hollow at the bow. Obviously, where the bow portion of the displacement curve is hollow, it is essential that the boat's center of gravity should be thrown as far aft as possible, in order to keep her head from burying when running under a press of sail; and this entails putting the midship section as far aft as possible; all of which doubtless had much to do with the adoption of the coefficients .60 and .55 above-mentioned.

But in the case of *Spray*, it will be noted that the displacement curve of the boat's entrance is not hollow at all, but convex. Therefore, there is no reason for throwing her center of gravity very far aft, because her bow is powerful enough to lift her at all times and under all circumstances. On the other hand, in *Spray*, there is a very good reason for not throwing the center of gravity very far aft of the middle of the L. W. L. And the reason is this: To throw the center of gravity aft, is to throw the midship section aft, and as the boat of necessity has great displacement, the placing of the midship section very far aft would result in hard lines (either buttocks, water-lines, or diagonals), and would produce a form of run that would inevitably create a heavy stern wave and make a slow boat.

The next element to be considered is the center of lateral resistance. This center lies .044 of the L. W. L. aft of station 18 when the boat is at rest. And here it is well to remember that the position of the C. L. R. is not always thoroughly appreciated in all its aspects. The C. L. R. as laid out on the drawings represents the point on which the boat (rudder and all) would balance if pushed sideways through the water. Take the case now under discussion. Suppose you were to make a working model of *Spray* and put her in a tank of still water. Then suppose you took the point of a knife, and pressed it against the side of the model at the exact point marked "C. L. R. at rest" in the drawing. Now, if you pushed the model sideways, at right angles to her keel, she would just balance on the knife point, the boat moving bodily sideways, without turning either the stern or the bow. And that is all that is meant by the C. L. R. as shown on the plans.

The instant, however, that the boat starts to move forward, the C. L. R. starts to move forward toward the bow of the boat. This is in obedience to a well-known law. As the bow works in solid water, and the stern dead-wood in broken water, the bow holds on better than the stern, and a square foot of lateral plane at the bow holds better than a square foot of lateral plane at the stern. The net result is that the effective C. L. R. moves forward. The question of *just how far* the C. L. R. moves forward when the boat begins to move ahead is a question involving some rather tedious calculation. Froude compiled a set of figures, showing the change of resistance per square foot at various portions of a surface located at various distances aft from the leading edge. (They relate specifically to skin resistance, but I assume that the lateral resistance would vary in the same ratio.) A table of these coefficients is given at page 135 of Mackrow's Pocket Book. Froude gives the figures for 2, 8, 20 and 50 feet. By interpolation, using a variable differential to satisfy the points established by Froude, it is possible to get the correct coefficient for any intermediate point. Then by applying the appropriate coefficients to the various stations of the immersed lateral plane, and applying Simpson's formula, it is possible to find how far the C. L. R. will move forward for any predetermined speed. In the specific case of *Spray*, moving at a speed of 6 knots, the C. L. R. moves, from a point 1.45 feet aft of station 18, to a point .4 of a foot aft of station 18, a forward movement of 1.05 feet. This gives us the actual working location of *Spray*'s C. L. R. at 6 knots, *disregarding the bow wave*. In order to make our calculation complete, we must further reckon with the bow wave. The question of stern wave may be disregarded, because, from the pictures and photographs of *Spray* underway, it clearly appears that the boat creates no sensible stern wave—she has too clean a run for that. She does raise a moderate bow wave, and the effect of that bow wave is of course to bring her effective C. L. R. a little bit forward.

The question of just exactly how far forward the bow wave will carry the C. L. R. is a matter beyond the ken of precise calculation. Judging from the height of the bow wave as shown on *Spray's* pictures, I should say it would amount to a little over 1% of the L. W. L., and if that assumption is correct, it would bring *Spray's* effective working C. L. R. exactly on station 18. Of course, every heave of the sea, every slant of wind, every touch on the helm throws this center a little bit forward or aft—it is no more fixed and stable than her angle of heel is fixed and stable. Constantly it plays forward and aft, but the central average point of its play must be station 18 or within a fraction of an inch of it.

In order to make my analysis of *Spray's* hull quite complete, I also calculated a center that is seldom considered at all in yacht design, and yet which must have some significance—that is, the center of wetted surface. In other words, I determined the effective center of her curve of immersed girths by Simpson's formula. To my surprise, this center worked out to a hair on identically the same line as the C. L. R. at rest, viz., 1.45 feet aft of station 18—another of the extraordinary coincidences in *Spray's* design.

Now exactly the same considerations which apply to the C. L. R. apply also to this center of wetted surface. In other words, when the boat begins to move forward, the focal point of her skin resistance begins to move forward from the place occupied by the center of wetted surface at rest. Thus, by applying Froude and Simpson, as in the case of the lateral plane, we find that at a speed of 6 knots, *Spray's* center of skin resistance moves forward from a point 1.45 aft of station 18, to a point .6 of a foot aft of station 18, a forward movement of .85 foot—that is, leaving the bow wave out of account. To complete our calculation, we must again reckon with the bow wave.

Now the bow wave will have a more potent effect in carrying forward the center of skin resistance, than in carrying forward the center of lateral resistance. And for this reason—the boat throws off two bow waves, one from the weather bow and one from the lee bow. Both of these waves affect the wetted surface, whereas only the lee wave affects the lateral plane. Of course, the wave on the lee bow is heavier than the wave on the weather bow, and therefore we may safely say that the two bow waves will *not* move the center of skin resistance forward twice as far as the lee-bow wave moves the C. L. R. forward. We thus reach the conclusion that the boat's wave action will throw the center of skin resistance forward further than the C. L. R. is thrown forward, and yet not so much

257

as twice that distance. We have already seen that the wave action throws her C. L. R. forward .4 of a foot. Therefore the wave action will throw her center of skin resistance forward between .4 and .8 of a foot, say .6 of a foot as a mean. And when we do move her center of skin resistance forward .6 of a foot, we land again exactly to a hair on station 18. Another in the series of coincidences.

ELEMENTS OF THE YAWL "SPRAY"

CALCULATED BY C. ANDRADE, JR., DEC. 1908

SCALE $\frac{1}{2}'' = 1'$

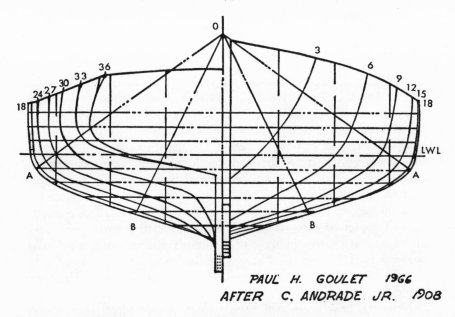

PAUL H. GOULET 1966
AFTER C. ANDRADE JR. 1908

Length O.A.	41'0¾" (36'9" excluding Figurehead)
Length L.W.L.	32'1"
Beam Extreme	14'1" (13'10" at L.W.L.)
Draught	4'1"
Freeboard (excluding Rail)	
Bow	4'1"
Waist	1'9¾"
Stern	2'9¾"
Rail	1'2"
Area Mid. Section Immersed	26.32 sq. ft.
Area Lat. Plane Immersed	111.88 sq. ft.
Area L.W.L. Plane	349.04 sq. ft.

258

Area Wetted Surface   443.18 sq. ft.
Area Rudder   7.52 sq. ft.
Sail Area Actual   1161.   sq. ft.
    Jib   246 sq. ft.
    Mainsail   604 sq. ft.
    Mizzen   151 sq. ft.
    Flying Jib   160 sq. ft.
Displacement   556.72 cu. ft.—35,658 lbs.
Lbs. per inch Immersion at L.W.L. = 1863

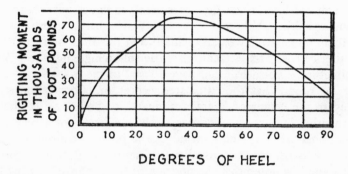

DEGREES OF HEEL

Even the effective center of the L. W. L. plane falls only .4 foot aft of station 18 when the boat is at rest; and the piling up of the bow waves under the bow, when she is underway, must bring this center also just about on station 18. (Unlike the C. L. R. and the center of skin resistance, the effective center of the L. W. L. plane is not affected by the forward motion of the boat—it is affected only by the bow wave.)

From an inspection of the L. W. L. plane, the almost perfect symmetry of the curve of displacement with reference to station 18 as an axis, and the symmetry of the boat's ends, it is quite evident that the longitudinal metacenter for a given angle of pitch forward will be at practically the same height as for an equal angle of pitch aft.

I know of no other conceivable factor of weight, displacement, buoyancy or resistance that can be calculated for a hull, so far as longitudinal balance is concerned, and I shall leave the discussion of *Spray*'s hull with the statement that every one of these factors, when she is underway, is concentrated exactly at her midship section (station 18). So much for *Spray*'s hull.

Let us now examine her sail plan.

At the outset, it should be remarked that the flying jib will be

259

eliminated from the discussion of sail balance, as it is a light-weather sail, set standing on a light bamboo jibboom, which is merely lashed to the bowsprit when the flying jib is set, and is stowed when the flying jib is stowed, and is never used on the wind.

When *Spray* is on the wind, she carries three sails only, the jib, mainsail and mizzen. The combined center of effort of these three sails at rest falls about .17 of a foot forward of the C. L. R. at rest. This .17 of a foot is only a little over .5 of 1% of the L. W. L. Modern practice calls for from 1 to 3% of the L. W. L. But it must be remembered that the 1 to 3% coefficient is used for sloops with large mainsails and small jibs. Whereas *Spray* is a yawl with an unusually large jib and a comparatively small mainsail. On this state of facts no less an authority than Dixon Kemp uses the following language ("Yacht Architecture," Third Edition, page 100): "In the case of yawls it is generally found that the calculated center of effort requires (relatively to the center of lateral resistance) to be a little further aft than in either cutters or schooners, as the mizzen is not a very effective sail on a wind, the eddy wind of the mainsail causing it to lift; also a yawl's mainmast is usually further forward than a cutter's, and it should be noted that the position of the center of effort of the largest driving sail influences the position of the general C. E. more than the calculation shows."

Spray's center of effort is therefore amply justified by authority, and the authority, in turn, is justified by *Spray*'s actual performance under the sail plan shown. For Slocum says of her: "Briefly, I have to say that when close-hauled in a light wind under all sail she required little or no weather helm. As the wind increased I would go on deck, if below, and turn the wheel up a spoke more or less, relash it, or as sailors say, put it in a becket, and then leave it as before."

Of course, in order to attain this balance, *Spray*'s efficient center of effort must be over her effective C. L. R. And as we have already seen that the effective C. L. R. at 6 knots falls exactly on station 18, so her efficient center of effort also at that speed must fall exactly on station 18.

It is obvious that, just as the effective C. L. R. moves forward as the boat moves forward so the efficient center of effort moves forward on the sail plan when the boat sails forward. This has long been known by naval architects; and the recent activity in aeroplane flight has led to much experiment on the subject. The C. E. seems to move forward more slowly than the C. L. R. as the boat's speed increases; and the result is that although the C. E. at rest is forward of the C. L. R., yet when the boat is at her normal speed, these two centers, advancing at unequal rates, come into exact balance; and when the boat's speed is increased still more by a harder wind, the C. L. R. continuing to work forward faster than the C. E. makes the boat carry a harder and harder weather helm as the wind increases. This is a matter of common observation.

CURVE OF STABILITY, TRANSVERSE METACENTRIC, ETC.

The curve of stability shows that *Spray* is theoretically uncapsizable, because of 90° of heel, she still has left a righting moment of over 20,000 foot-pounds or over 9 foot-tons. This is most remarkable for a boat of her shallow draught; doubly remarkable in view of the fact that she carries no outside ballast whatever, and even her inside ballast consists merely of cement blocks. (All boatmen of experience say that stone or cement ballast makes a livelier, "corkier" boat than the same weight of lead or iron.) Her maximum stability is at about 35° of heel, where she has a righting moment of 75,000 foot-pounds or over 33 foot-tons.

As she should never be sailed much lower than 10° of heel, it will be seen that she has an ample margin of safety at all times.

In plotting the curve of stability, I assumed the center of gravity to lie exactly at the L. W. L., which, I think, is conservative.

I have also plotted the transverse L. W. L., transverse center of buoyancy, and metacentric height for each 10° of heel up to 90°.

CONCLUSION

I conclude my analysis of *Spray*'s lines with a feeling of profound admiration and respect. She is not only an able boat, but a beautiful boat; using the term "beautiful" as defined by Charles Elliott Norton, "that form most perfectly adapted to perform its allotted work"—beautiful in the same sense that Sandow, or the Farnese Hercules is beautiful. From the man who loves boats and the sea, and in some measure understands them (for it has been given to no one yet to know all their ways), *Spray* will receive the recognition that is her due.

She is the perfection of her type—a perfection demonstrated not only on paper, but by the ordeal of actual achievement. She is an oceangoing cruiser, in the largest sense of that term. After sailing 46,000 miles, and weathering a hundred gales, some of which foundered great ships in his near vicinity, Slocum says of her: "I have given in the plans of *Spray* the dimensions of such a ship as I

261

should call seaworthy in all conditions of weather and on all seas." These words coming from such a source are not lightly to be disregarded.

The question is one of such interest, that THE RUDDER invites the opinions of all amateur and professional designers and practical boatmen, to see if they would suggest any departures whatever from *Spray*'s lines in a boat intended to circumnavigate the globe single-handed.

Of course, if the question were to design the best possible boat to race on Long Island Sound, or to Block Island, or even to Bermuda, there is no question but what other characteristics than those of *Spray* would be adopted.

But let the question be clearly apprehended—what would be the best boat with which to circumnavigate the globe single-handed? Would the ideal boat for that purpose depart in any measure from *Spray*'s lines; and if so, why?

On this question, a full discussion will be of the utmost interest.

We trust that all who are interested will contribute their views, and not only their views but their reasons for their views.

INDEX

267

About the Author

KENNETH E. SLACK, yachtsman and writer, is Australian Vice-Commodore of the Slocum Society and a frequent contributor to its journal, *The Spray*, as well as to *Rudder, Seacraft, Yachting Monthly*, and other sailing publications. Mr. Slack graduated from the University of Sydney in 1953 with honors in organic chemistry, and has since been actively engaged in research and manufacture in the paint industry. He has also served as scientific officer with the Maritime Services Board of New South Wales. An experienced deep-water sailor, he has cruised throughout Australian waters, including several extended ocean voyages. He plans to build his own copy of the *Spray* in the near future.